THE WILD REALM:

Animals of East Africa

By Louis S. B. Leakey
Foreword by Leonard Carmichael, *Vice President for Research and Exploration,*
National Geographic Society

Produced by the National Geographic Special Publications Division,
Robert L. Breeden, *Chief*

National Geographic Society, Washington, D. C.
Melvin M. Payne, *President*
Melville Bell Grosvenor, *Editor-in-Chief*
Frederick G. Vosburgh, *Editor*

THE WILD REALM:
ANIMALS OF EAST AFRICA
By LOUIS S. B. LEAKEY

Published by
THE NATIONAL GEOGRAPHIC SOCIETY
MELVIN M. PAYNE, *President*
MELVILLE BELL GROSVENOR, *Editor-in-Chief*
FREDERICK G. VOSBURGH, *Editor*
GILBERT M. GROSVENOR, *Executive Editor*
  for this series
WILLIAM GRAVES, *Consulting Editor*
  for this book

Prepared by
THE SPECIAL PUBLICATIONS DIVISION
ROBERT L. BREEDEN, *Editor*
DONALD J. CRUMP, *Associate Editor*
PHILIP B. SILCOTT, *Manuscript Editor*
MARY ANN HARRELL, *Project Editor*
LOUISE GRAVES, CYNTHIA R. RAMSAY,
  TEE LOFTIN SNELL, PEGGY D.
  WINSTON, *Research*
LINDA M. SEEMAN, *Illustrations Research*
RONALD M. FISHER, WILLIAM R. GRAY, JR.,
  LEON M. LARSON, *Picture Legends*
JUDITH C. FORD, CAROL R. TEACHEY,
  SANDRA A. TURNER, BARBARA J. WALKER,
  Editorial Assistants

Illustrations and Design
DAVID R. BRIDGE, *Picture Editor*
JOSEPH A. TANEY, *Art Director*
JOSEPHINE B. BOLT, *Assistant Art Director*
JAY H. MATTERNES, *Illustrator for this book*
JOHN D. GARST, MUNRO KINSEY,
  Map Research

Production and Printing
ROBERT W. MESSER, *Production*
JUDY L. STRONG, *Production Assistant*
JAMES R. WHITNEY, *Engraving and Printing*
JOHN R. METCALFE, *Assistant, Engraving*
  and Printing
DOROTHY M. CORSON, *Index*

---

*Balancing easily on her hind legs, a slender
gerenuk stands 7 feet tall to browse. Overleaf: Lions stride past a watchful Thomson's
gazelle at dawn on Tanzania's Serengeti
Plain. Page 1: Stealthy black leopard
snarls menacingly.*

M. P. KAHL (RIGHT); GEORGE B. SCHALLER, NEW YORK
ZOOLOGICAL SOCIETY (OVERLEAF); DAVID R. BRIDGE,
NATIONAL GEOGRAPHIC STAFF (PAGE ONE)

Foreword

Animals of East Africa is a remarkable book for three very good reasons. First, the animals it presents are as a group probably the most dramatically interesting of all the world's organisms. Second, the author, Dr. Louis Seymour Bazett Leakey, is one of the renowned scientists of our age. Third, the many new pictures in this volume are especially fine—both the splendid photographs and the paintings that show fossil African animals as they almost certainly looked when they roamed its plains and forests eons ago. These paintings are by Mr. Jay H. Matternes—a gifted artist and a scientific student of fossil animals. It is not an exaggeration to call him the modern Audubon of prehistoric mammals.

Dr. Leakey is world-famous as an anthropologist, paleontologist, and student of man's prehistory. He is also—and this is by no means characteristic of all zoologists—a lifelong lover of animals.

His unique boyhood fostered this love. His father, the late Harry Leakey, and his mother were among the first Anglican missionaries in East Africa. Young Louis spent many hours with boys of the Kikuyu tribe, and he studied the ways of game with a Dorobo hunter. The Kikuyu's language was his language, their intuitive knowledge of animals was his knowledge. Even today, he has told me, he often thinks not in English but in Kikuyu as he watches the great animals of his land.

After undergraduate days at Cambridge University in England, the author went on to become a Fellow of St. John's College and to earn his Ph.D. Back in East Africa, he took up the quest he has pursued unflaggingly: the search for very early man and his long-vanished world. In this, as everyone knows, he and his family and associates have made discoveries of profound importance.

Whenever scientists explore wholly new fields, novel facts appear that call established theories into question and emerging concepts give new significance to accepted data. In such periods of debate we see science at its most exciting, and this book appears at such a time.

How animals behave in their natural habitats is the subject of ethology. Today many trained observers of this school are reporting in a new way the lives of Africa's wonderful animals and bringing us new insight into their patterns of behavior. Thus Dr. Leakey's account, drawing on years of field experience, is of special interest.

Even more is this true of his contributions to our knowledge of our own ancestors and all the hominids of the past—our kindred now extinct. In this field our views are changing with dramatic speed; but it is certain that Dr. Leakey's discoveries, and his interpretations, will always be a noteworthy chapter in the story of man before written history. He never forgets that man became man in a world of animals.

Thus his understanding of man and of animals has an added dimension. His scientific mind sees animals through trained Dorobo eyes. Therefore anyone who reads this book and looks at its unrivaled illustrations will gain a very special kind of understanding of the balanced and interrelated life patterns of the mammals of East Africa—and how Dr. Leakey and other conservationists are fighting to save this unique and truly arch-royal part of the world's endangered animal kingdom.

LEONARD CARMICHAEL
Vice President for Research and Exploration,
National Geographic Society

Night prowler, the leopard haunts dense bush and forest in search of prey. This big cat finds refuge in the Serengeti National Park, one of the protected lands that safeguard Africa's priceless heritage of wildlife.

M. P. KAHL

Contents

1

The Richest Garden

As a boy roaming the bush country around my home in Kenya, I took wild animals very much for granted. They were simply part of the natural surroundings. Leopards were common, though rarely seen because they kept a wary distance from man. These powerful cats preyed on wild pigs and small antelopes and also raided the flocks of Kikuyu tribesmen to carry away sheep and goats. I can't remember that as children my two older sisters, my younger brother, and I were ever warned against the leopards—or any other dangerous animal. The accepted view was that if you left them alone, they would leave you alone.

Once we had two playful leopard cubs brought to us. They had been taken from their lair by a Kikuyu boy while the mother was away. Despite our bitter disappointment, Father would not allow us to keep them. Such pets, when grown, could turn dangerous. We regularly reared baby duiker and occasionally brown, soft-eyed bushbuck which we found abandoned or which Kikuyu herdboys found and brought to us.

We always, in fact, had a variety of wild animals as pets as well as several dogs and many cats. Through the years we had a number of monkeys, one a black-and-white colobus that looked like a tiny wizened old man. Our changing menagerie included hares, serval cats, and small wide-eyed galagos, or bushbabies. There were also some semi-tame genets, small nocturnal predators that adopted us, more or less.

Largely because of my close association with wild animals, I developed a lifelong interest in them. But there was also another reason. I was the son of missionary parents working with the Kikuyu tribe, and so I learned to speak Kikuyu as fluently as English and heard many times the people's folktales and stories, many of them about animals.

During my childhood, I spent countless hours with Kikuyu friends. Often in early evening I would sit with other boys in the compound outside one of the elders' huts and listen to tales of tribal raids, traditional history, and the coming of the white man. The animal fables, which I enjoyed most, were chiefly recounted by married women with prodigious memories. A tale I vividly recall tells of a race between a hare and a chameleon for the hand of a beautiful maiden. The first to sit on a stool placed at the finish line would be the winner. The chameleon, hopelessly outclassed, knew he had to outwit his rival. As the race began he grabbed tightly on to the hare's tail and rode with him to the finish. When the hare spun around to sit, the chameleon, of course, was underneath, first to reach the stool and therefore winner of the maiden's hand.

The stories about animals seldom dealt with hunting or trapping; these tribesmen have long regarded virtually all wild animals as unclean and not fit for use as food. The only creatures exempt from this taboo were the buffalo, the large antelope called eland, and, for some mysterious reason, the ant-eating aardvark.

Since the tribe disdained hunting I learned the skills of stalking animals from an old man of the Dorobo people, Joshua Muhia, who lived among the Kikuyu. Joshua knew well the ways of wild animals, but his Kikuyu friends wanted no part of his lore. Even his own son, wishing to grow up a proper Kikuyu, shunned hunting and had little interest in what Joshua did. I, however, became a willing pupil.

From Joshua I learned to camouflage my human form with leaves and small branches; to approach a quarry diagonally, and very alertly,

Cloud-wreathed Kilimanjaro, highest of Africa's mountains at 19,340 feet, looms beyond a black rhinoceros in Kenya's Masai Amboseli Game Reserve. The rhino, often needing several square miles to supply its food requirements, might well symbolize the major concern of Africa's conservationists: preserving the enormous areas required by many wild creatures, in the face of man's increasing demand for more land.

9

and above all never to show my hands or arms. Most important, I learned patience, for it was necessary to get quite close to an animal if it was to be killed with the Dorobo's short-range weapons—the bow and arrow, thrusting spear, or club.

My friend and teacher also showed me how to make noose traps and how to capture a small antelope by building a low fence of branches around three sides of its lair while it was away feeding. Such a fence need only be strong enough to make the animal pause. It must not be so visible that the returning quarry will become suspicious. Once the animal has settled in and begun to relax, the hunter creeps close, then dashes in to grab it as it hesitates at the fence before trying to escape.

I once caught a duiker in this way, and I remember that at the moment I hurled myself upon the animal and realized I actually had it gripped tightly in my hands, I experienced the primitive hunter's thrill.

G UIDED BY JOSHUA, I learned to read the signs that in Africa can mean survival—a sudden stillness, the mark of a footprint scarcely visible in the grass, a torn leaf, a broken spider web, a rustle in the bushes. Many of the Dorobo's lessons have served me well to this day. I am often aware of the nearness of animals when others with me have noticed nothing at all. As a paleontologist, too, I have used much of what I learned when trying to interpret the possible ways Stone Age man hunted and trapped his prey.

I first became interested in Stone Age man at age 13, when I read a fascinating book by H. N. Hall called *Days Before History.* In it Hall told the story of the late Stone Age people of Britain, inspiring me to start an immediate search for stone implements in the area of my home. I soon found many flakes, scrapers, and other simple tools of obsidian and chert in washouts and along roads where the surface soil had been eroded or cut away. My Kikuyu friends laughed at me for suggesting that these flaked stones were the work of men long ago and insisted that they actually were *nyenji cia ngoma*—the discarded razors of the spirits of the sky. My parents, too, did not accept them as evidence of early man.

My deepening interest in prehistory eventually took me to Cambridge University in England, where I studied anthropology and archeology. I also took courses in zoology and paleontology, since it was essential that I be able to identify and interpret the fossil animal bones that I hoped to excavate, one day, in East Africa. This study greatly expanded my understanding of the animal kingdom, for I learned that zoologists in classifying animals compare them with fossils as well as with other living forms. Sometimes fossil studies reveal unsuspected relationships among living creatures and help determine whether an animal belongs to one genus or another.

Moreover, just as the study of fossils leads to a better understanding of living species, so does the study of the anatomy, behavior, and habitat of living forms help immensely in solving the mysteries of animal remains that have lain buried in the rocks for millions of years.

Overleaf: Burchell's zebras, ill at ease near tall reeds that may conceal lions, splash through a rainpool in the Amboseli Reserve. Known in Swahili as punda milia, *or striped donkey, this zebra stubbornly resists domestication.*

M. P. KAHL

Forbidding coast and rugged interior kept much of East Africa a blank on maps for centuries. Only within the past 100 years did European settlers move inland. By the end of 1968, Kenya, Tanzania, and Uganda had set aside some 70 game reserves, parks, and sanctuaries for the continent's incomparable wildlife.

MAP BY BOBBY G. CROCKETT, GEOGRAPHIC ART DIVISION

Sometimes I am asked to name my favorite among the animals—an impossible task. East Africa has a staggering array of creatures, each equally fascinating in its own way. This great wildlife population is, I believe, unmatched anywhere else on earth. Incredible in its complexity, it evolved on a continent that for millions of years provided optimum conditions for life somewhere on its surface, even when undergoing volcanic upheavals and climatic changes and alterations of sea level. Because there was always some optimum area the creatures of East Africa evolved with less natural disturbance than in many other places, and today enjoy an almost unbelievable variety of habitats.

Steamy mangrove swamps fringe parts of the Indian Ocean shore; tropical forests along permanent streams merge into the coastal plains. Expanses of hot, dry bushland, open grassland, and near-desert stretch steeply inland. From highland plateaus often covered in forest, magnificent mountains rise thousands of feet, with the highest, snow-mantled Kilimanjaro, attaining 19,340 feet. Volcanic eruptions raised Kilimanjaro, and many of the East African mountains; others, like those in the Ruwenzori range—the fabled Mountains of the Moon where some peaks reach above 16,000 feet—were thrust upward at a time when the Great Rift Valley was sinking.

Bands of vegetation ring the mountains, changing as the elevation increases. On their flanks grow dense montane forests of juniper and cone-bearing *Podocarpus* trees, the haunt of elephants, bongo, and giant forest hogs. In the glades various grasses provide grazing for buffalo. Around 8,000 to 10,000 feet a zone of bamboo girdles many of the mountains. Finally, separating the bamboo zone from the barren slopes of the peaks, are the wind-scoured moorlands, where giant heath-trees, lichens, mosses, and groundsels shape a bizarre landscape.

In all this vast range, where food supply, climate, and shelter combine to create livable environments, numerous species occupy their own special place. While many may share the same habitat, and to some extent compete for food, no two species utilize the living area in exactly the same way. Zebra, wildebeest, hartebeest, and some species of gazelle, for example, grazing on a luxuriant pasture, might seem to the casual observer to be a random mixture eating the same food. Actually each species has its own preferred foods, either different plants, or different stages of growth of the same plants. Zebras move into the high grass, shortening the stems and trampling the growth. Wildebeest and hartebeest crop the grass still shorter. Tender new shoots then sprout, attracting the gazelles. In this way all the animals have a share of the same pastureland, but each uses it differently.

One sees large animals only in certain parts of East Africa—a fact that was also true during my boyhood, but for different reasons. In those days there was more game than now, much of it in areas nearly devoid of large animals today because man has taken over the land, but there were few roads and no cars, and thus game areas were hard to

Masai tribesman, with spear and herding staff, rounds up strays on badly overgrazed pasture in Kenya. Cattle mean wealth to the Masai, who drink a mixture of blood and milk, but rarely kill the animals for meat. Increasing numbers of cattle often destroy the habitats of wild animals.

Overleaf: Zebra and wildebeest, part of a vast migrating army of animals, pause to graze during their march across the Serengeti Plain, on Tanzania's central plateau. In the dry season, eastern park areas become devoid of big game as the animals move north and west to better water and forage.

M. P. KAHL

reach. It was only the determined hunters who set out to find big game, usually on horseback or on foot. Because of the hunters the animals had grown wary of man. Today, however, large animals amble about in protected parks easily accessible to visitors.

My mother, who lived in Kikuyu country more than half a century, never saw a live lion or an elephant or a rhinoceros, and only once did she see a leopard in the wild. In fact, she never saw buffalo or eland or many of the common animals. That is not really as surprising as it might seem. She lived most of her life in Africa on the mission station, and in the earlier days when she traveled she reclined in a hammock carried by two to four men along well-worn trails — hardly the conveyance from which to view big game!

17

R. D. ESTES (ABOVE); SARA CONN THOMPSON

It would have been possible, of course, in my childhood days to follow roundabout footpaths from my home at Kabete to the game-covered plains beyond what is now the Langata suburb of Nairobi, but it would have been unwise. The plains held not only game but also Masai warriors armed with spears, who might have mistaken the members of such a party for intruders or would-be stock raiders. Even without the risk of such an encounter, it would have taken most of a day for the return trip. Now I could drive from Kabete to Nairobi National Park in 20 minutes.

From time to time our whole family would make the trek from Kabete to the Church Missionary Society mission operated by my uncle and aunt in Nairobi, then a small town on the railroad. Not far from my uncle's we had to pass a large swamp, reputed to be the haunt of many lions. I never saw any of the great cats then, but I sometimes heard them roaring during the night. Today the lions are gone; the swamp, drained and built over, is the site of a road intersection near the University College of Nairobi and the famous Norfolk Hotel. The roars instead are man-made—traffic streaming on Uhuru Highway, along which I drive to reach my office at the Centre for Prehistory and Palaeontology. Planes from an airport a few miles away often fly overhead.

Although I had heard lions occasionally, I never saw one alive until 1929, when I was 26 years old. I was coming back to Kenya with my wife and two staff members by lorry from Johannesburg, South Africa, where we had attended a meeting of the British Association for the Advancement of Science. We had reached a point just 15 miles outside Nairobi—after a round trip of 5,000 miles over rough, often gullied tracks—and we hadn't seen a single lion. Then suddenly they were all around us. Four lionesses lay on the road about 60 yards ahead, and we counted eight cats on either side. We had kept a sharp watch for lions throughout our journey because we wanted to get some photographs of the animals. Our elation at seeing them, however, turned to uneasiness when the four lionesses on the road started toward us at a low crouch, their tails switching menacingly. The driver swerved from the road and speeded up to outdistance the cats as they bounded after us.

We used no film that day. I personally seldom take photos, but I believe that the camera is the only way to "shoot" game. Hunting with a gun never had much appeal for me. Father occasionally shot a duck, partridge, or pigeon for the pot, and for a few years I did some shooting too. After the age of about 20 I shot only for food or for the protection of life, and since the late 1930's I've not shot at all.

Through the years I've seen a gradual, but very significant, change for the better in hunting safaris. Today far fewer people hunt with guns, and more and more of them thrill to the difficult and sometimes dangerous sport of hunting with a camera. Of course hunting parties do still go out after big-game heads as trophies—but many safari organizers no longer accept clients who want to kill animals. Many, like my son Richard, advertise "photographic and viewing safaris only."

The experienced camera hunter works to get a picture that is not only good in quality but which also reveals something about his subject's behavior. He may, for example, catch sight of a giraffe in a head-down straddle-legged posture and assume it's at a water hole. As he stealthily moves closer, however, he finds that the giraffe is not drinking, but eating saline earth to get the mineral it needs.

The animal must spread wide its forelegs and lower its head just as it does when drinking; but while it can suck water up its long neck, it cannot do the same thing with dry, salty earth. As the photographer records the giraffe's efforts he notices that the animal gets a cheek-bulging mouthful, then lifts its head to chew, soften, and gradually swallow the saline earth. The photographer has bagged a real trophy, and the stately giraffe is left unharmed, perhaps to be "shot" by other camera hunters before the day is out.

I'm sure that very few photographers realize how valuable their pictures might be as an aid in animal studies. In the mid-1960's zoologist J. B. Foster, now in Canada with the British Columbia Provincial Museum at Victoria, learned to recognize nearly 220 individual giraffes in the Nairobi National Park by studying the animals' skin patterns. Setting up a card file that included photographs of the left side of the neck and head of each giraffe, Dr. Foster was able to record the animals' activities. The skin patterns do not change markedly with age and are as distinctive as human fingerprints. Foster has recognized the same animal seen in photographs taken more than 20 years apart.

He says that since the Nairobi Park giraffes are frequently photographed, he could build up an unsurpassed record of the animals if every visitor who got a satisfactory picture of a giraffe in the park would supply him with a copy and a note of the date it was taken. Over the years such a file would yield invaluable data concerning the giraffe's life span and rate of growth, the incidence of births and deaths, and the relationships of herds and individuals. Such information is vital, for if we are to conserve wildlife, we must learn what conditions are best for the survival of each species.

One of the rewards of repeated animal observation is that at any moment you may see a creature engaged in an activity you've never witnessed before and so learn a new facet of animal behavior. Such study is not only a task for the ethologist, or professional animal behaviorist, but also for any keen observer, who, even though he takes no photographs, can report what he has seen to park authorities.

In the past, game watching was not easy. Animals knew man only as a hunter and they fled at the sight or scent of him. Today, in the great national parks, many of the wild creatures virtually ignore cars, or simply express curiosity, for they have learned that people in cars are not a source of danger. Wildlife photographers and observers can get within a few yards of their subjects, near enough to take really beautiful pictures without telephoto lenses or other expensive equipment. In non-park areas, however, most animals still flee at the approach of a car. All too often it carries a hunter ready to jump out and kill.

Visitors to Africa's parks not only can venture among lions, elephants, rhinos, and a seemingly endless variety of antelopes but also can record their unforgettable experiences with motion-picture and still cameras. More and more visitors make careful notes of what they see, and some even take along tape recorders to capture the sounds of animals—the roars, grunts, and squeals, the barking call of an alarmed zebra herd on the move, or the noisy, croaking chorus of vultures feeding on carrion.

In nature's harsh but efficient system some must die that others may live. Above, a wilde-

BARON HUGO VAN LAWICK (TOP AND RIGHT); M. P. KAHL

beest tries vainly to protect her newborn calf from a hyena. Courageous and robust, wildebeest may even fight back when attacked by lions, but a successful defense is rare. An infant barely half an hour old (below left) struggles to rise; within minutes it began following the herd. Below, spotted hyenas devour a wildebeest calf.

I can't overemphasize the importance of accurate animal observation. So much remains to be learned about African wildlife, despite the fact that the continent's remarkable creatures have long fascinated the curious. In the late 19th and early 20th century a number of hunters and game wardens described the animals they saw and conscientiously recorded individual examples of behavior and general data on distribution, habitat, and diet. But such scattered observations, helpful as they are, can give us only limited information.

FOR KNOWLEDGE in depth we need many more trained students of animal behavior dedicated to making long and exhaustive studies. The ethologist does much more than merely look at animals. He must rather live in very close association with them until they accept him, sometimes even allowing him close enough to touch them. Some animals, out of curiosity, have even ventured to touch or sniff at their observer!

While gaining his subjects' acceptance, the observer learns to recognize each individual by sight, as Dr. Foster did with the giraffes. This recognition is one of the most distinctive features of modern study. Only when the observer has achieved it can he begin to work out the size and stability of his study group, trace the interactions of individuals to determine which animals are dominant at any given time, and learn exactly what the animals eat and how they obtain their food.

A number of observers are now documenting the numerous variations of one behavior pattern shared by many creatures: territoriality. Although there are exceptions, individual males of many species lay claim to an area—whether on the ground, in the water, or among the branches of a tree—primarily for breeding purposes.

Each creature defines its borders in one or more ways—with noise, with urine and glandular secretions and dung heaps; the area becomes in a very real sense the creature's property. An owner exerts great energy and cunning to retain exclusive possession, to defend its holding against rivals within its own species.

A territorial male will normally fight more vigorously for his space than for his mates. The defender seems to have a psychological advantage, for usually he can drive away a challenger at the border of his territory with nothing more than posturings, violent gestures, and noises. Battles with invaders, although very serious, rarely end in death. If a creature is killed it is usually by misadventure.

Ornithologists first recognized the existence of territorial behavior in wild creatures. A century ago Bernard Altum of Germany set forth the theory that a male bird does not fight for females but for an area he has marked off as his own; his song expresses not joy but a warning against intrusion by others of his kind. An Englishman, H. Eliot Howard, in his book *Territory in Bird Life*, published in 1920, gave many examples to prove that Altum's territorial theory was indeed fact. Since that time numerous researchers, my friend Sir Julian Huxley and his colleague Ashley Montagu among them, have recorded the territorial

Like a house cat, a caracal toys with his prey, a mole rat he pulled from the mouth of its burrow. This cat strikes so swiftly that it can kill several birds—such as doves and sandgrouse—before the flock gets off the ground, then leap into the air and grab still another. Caracals prowl largely at night, preying also on hares, rodents, and small antelopes.

Overleaf: Rare white giraffe gallops with its herd across Tanzania's Rukwa Valley. Giraffes reach speeds of 30 miles an hour, but the measured rhythm of their legs makes them seem much slower, almost as if running in slow motion.

HELEN AND FRANK SCHREIDER, NATIONAL GEOGRAPHIC STAFF

ALAN ROOT

23

behavior of many more birds. Ethologists have now shown that mammals exhibit such behavior as well.

An astonishing example of territoriality was reported by Dr. Helmut K. Buechner, now head of the Office of Ecology, Smithsonian Institution, Washington, D. C. For decades naturalists had believed that the Uganda kob, a golden-brown lyre-horned antelope with white eye rings, bred in harems with a buck shepherding as many as 30 does and their young. In March 1957 Buechner's wife alerted him to what she thought might be territorial behavior on the part of a kob herd in northwestern Uganda. Later, during concentrated studies, Buechner determined that the animals mated not in harems but at a number of special breeding arenas.

A TYPICAL ARENA, some 200 yards in diameter, held a cluster of 12 to 15 heavily trampled territories varying from 8 to 15 yards across. In each stood a single buck, one of the elite of the male kobs. It is to such arenas, Buechner discovered, that the females go for mating.

Since the kob follows no breeding season, males occupy the arenas the year around. A buck must defend his territory unceasingly, bluffing with lowered head and flattened ears, or ramming rivals with a clash of horns. So fierce is the competition, in fact, that some males hold their plots less than a day, others for no more than a week or two. When a champion falls he joins a bachelor herd for several weeks or months of recuperation, then returns in an attempt to regain his lost territory.

What then of the supposed harems that generations of naturalists thought were breeding groups? Buechner found that although most males outside the arenas live in bachelor herds, some stake out large single territories of their own between the breeding grounds. He reports that females and their young may join such a buck at intervals during the day, but although there is much ceremonial mating activity, few of the does ever permit a complete mating act. When the does wander away to an adjacent territory the buck remains behind, content to watch them go and unwilling to relinquish his own holding.

In recent years National Geographic Society grants have substantially furthered research in animal behavior. The Society has sponsored such projects as the remarkable chimpanzee studies of Baroness Jane van Lawick-Goodall, work among Africa's mountain gorillas by the courageous Dian Fossey, and the antelope studies of Richard D. Estes.

Because so much remains to be learned, it will be many years before we can really claim to know what we need to know about how animals behave in the wild. I hope that this book will help the reader see East Africa's animals as I see them. I hope, too, to pass along some of the understanding of animals that I have gained in a lifetime in Africa — through stalking game at Joshua's side, through work in vertebrate paleontology, and through long association with the national parks and wildlife groups of East Africa. And finally I hope to inspire inquiring minds to go out and discover much more for themselves.

Ringed horns of a male waterbuck sweep back and outward, the smooth tips curving forward. Never found far from water, these rough-coated antelope usually travel in small herds made up largely of cows and their young.

26

ALAN ROOT

2

Last of the Giants

Elephants and buffalo had crowded the water hole and salt lick at Treetops, the famous game watchers' hotel on the southern slopes of Kenya's Aberdare Range. Visitors sat wrapped in blankets against the late-afternoon chill as buffalo drank noisily or wallowed in mud and came out splotched and glistening. A herd of some 40 elephants, mostly cows and calves, had taken over the salty area. Now and then a baby crowded its mother's forequarters to nurse, its slender trunk curled above its head. Older animals squelched over the moist ground. At intervals one would drive back an intruding buffalo with irritable squeals. Suddenly one guest murmured, "*It's prehistoric.*" He was right.

Nearly everywhere in the world, until relatively recent times, giant animals roamed the countryside, hunted by Stone Age man. Some eight or ten thousand years ago on the American continent hunters used pitfalls and stone-tipped spears against the now-extinct mastodon. In Europe men of the Ice Age encountered the woolly mammoth and various kinds of rhinoceroses; during warmer interglacial periods, hippopotamuses flourished in the Thames and the Somme. In Asia, too, strange animals lived side by side with early man: elephants quite unlike those domesticated in India today, and huge hippos. Africa had its giants too; and here, to a greater degree than elsewhere, some of them have survived.

Of these, the elephant, *Loxodonta africana*, is without doubt the best known and probably the most interesting. He and his Asian cousin (*Elephas maximus*) are the sole survivors of the Proboscidea, a group that once thrived in most of the world, except Australia.

Njogu, as we call the African elephant in Kikuyu, survived by virtue of an extraordinary adaptability to climate, habitat, and food supply. South of the Sahara, elephants range almost anywhere—except where man has driven them out or exterminated them. They are equally at home in semidesert, in forests and open woodlands, and on grassy plains.

Their food varies accordingly. The trunk, a highly modified nasal organ that merges into the upper lip, combines the work of nose and hand, and enables elephants to feed on many types of vegetation. I have watched elephants grip short clumps of grass, pull them up by the roots, beat them against their forelegs or chests to shake off the earth, and consume the plants whole. They pick leaves and twigs from all sorts of bushes and trees, and gather nuts and fruit from many palms. Often they break off large tree branches, then yank off ragged strips of bark with their trunks. A single delicacy may keep them at one spot for some time. Recently I came across a bull standing alone about 100 yards from the Nairobi-Mombasa highway. After loosening the soil with his tusks, he was tugging up small bushes and then slowly chewing the roots. I watched for nearly half an hour before driving on. Next day I passed the area again. To my surprise, the bull was still there, pulling up and eating more of the same sort of roots.

The quantity of food consumed depends on the nature and richness of the items available but may easily amount to several hundred pounds daily for an adult. Elephants spend much of their time feeding, and will travel immense distances to satisfy their needs. If necessary, they will move 30 or 40 miles overnight. They also seem very clever at locating underground water in apparently dry streambeds. Using tusks and

Young elephant and black rhinoceros browse in protected thornbush country in Kenya. In the wild these juveniles would follow adults of their own species. Park wardens often rescue orphaned animals, keep them to maturity, then release them in a park or other refuge. The adult elephant, fearing no animal but man, normally tolerates rhinos but at times will drive them away and may even kill them.

*Reddened by dust in Tsavo
National Park, Kenya, male
elephants joust with heavy
trunks and clattering tusks. A
bull (opposite) blows a cloud of
dust in his face after vacuum-
ing the ground with his trunk.
Elephants use their trunks to
gather food, spank their young,
and draw up water for drinking and spray baths; fingerlike
projections at the tip enable
them to pick up small objects.
At right, a cow nimbly
rubs her eye.*

31

forefeet, they dig until they can drink their fill. Under optimum conditions they will drink 35 to 50 gallons a day; they can do with less for a short period. Water left in these holes benefits other creatures.

Unfortunately elephants tend to be very destructive in their feeding habits. They push over a small tree and then eat only a few of its leaves. They break off branches and rip so much bark from a larger tree that it will die. They amble on and repeat the process, again and again. An area devastated by elephants may not recover for several years. This problem affects many East African parks, and specialists are carrying out intensive studies of the numbers and activities of these great creatures, trying to arrive at some solution. All of us who are concerned with the future of our parklands hope these studies will soon provide specific guidelines. Perhaps some elephants will have to be shot as a means of controlling their numbers within the parks, but I like to think that a better way can be found. Already, when herds migrate from protected areas, their numbers are sharply reduced by trophy hunters and poachers who kill the animals for ivory and meat as well as for the tail hairs, used in making bracelets worn as good-luck charms. The studies also should tell us more about elephant behavior, which varies from region to region, from herd to herd, and even from one individual to another.

BULL ELEPHANTS frequently go about in small groups, two or three or half a dozen together, while cows with young calves form family units of up to a dozen or so. Sometimes the family units congregate into large herds. Generally a few bulls accompany them. These herds deserve the greatest respect. I shall never forget the narrow escape I had with such a herd in 1924 on a British Museum expedition at Tendaguru Hill, then a remote spot in Tanganyika Territory. Shotgun in hand, I was trailing a covey of guinea fowl to get fresh meat for my men. The birds scuttled into thick bush, where I crawled slowly after them. A strange rumbling noise sounded, first on one side and then the other—I had crawled right in among the elephants! The nearest help was a mile away, but the best help isn't much in that kind of situation. My heart was beating very fast as I crawled away, as quietly and slowly as I could—if the cows had caught my scent they would almost certainly have charged and killed me.

According to an old, old story, elephants go off to a single remote spot when they sense death approaching. Visitors often ask me about this myth. I have never found any real basis for it, but I can think of two explanations. During the 19th century many Arab traders roamed East Africa in search of two things: ivory and slaves. Africans living near these trade routes would collect ivory and hide it in some thicket near their huts. I suspect that the first tale of an "elephant graveyard" arose when a white man found such a collection, misinterpreted it, and assumed that the tusks had survived while the bones had crumbled to dust. Moreover, at a few sites in East Africa poisonous gases sometimes

Elephants in Murchison Falls National Park, Uganda, browse as white cattle egrets wheel above. Two or three times a year dozens of small family units form such congregations for a couple of weeks; while together the animals become highly active and excitable. This herd, shown in part, numbered 500.

ALAN ROOT

emerge from vents in volcanic rock. At certain times escaping gas will suffocate any creature that comes near one of these places, particularly if it is in a small valley or depression. I know a photographer who was making a picture of one of the dead elephants at such a spot, luckily from a safe distance. As he watched, a hyena approached another carcass. Suddenly the hyena collapsed before his eyes and lay motionless — and the photographer retreated.

I F THE ELEPHANT is the best known and most interesting of the surviving giants, the giraffe probably attracts the most attention and causes the most surprised comment. When you see a giraffe for the first time, moving slowly through thornbush toward open country or in silhouette on the skyline, you can scarcely believe your eyes. He is so tall, so much taller than you expect. On roads through a national park you can study this lovely animal from a few yards away. Apart from a swing of the tail, a flick of the ears, a slight movement of the great eyes or twitching of the nose, he will stand quite motionless for a time and watch your stationary car. He looks haughty, and slightly condescending.

Then, quite calmly, he resumes his feeding or moves slowly away to join some companions a little farther off. Then you find that he is most surprisingly stately in his movements, when you would have expected ungainliness. The left legs come forward almost together, then the right; as the hoofs touch the ground the neck swings backward: a distinctive rhythm, like something in a dream. When giraffes break into a gallop, the long, powerful forelegs lunge forward, the legs stretch out, then bunch beneath the heavy body; the neck arches forward, then back. One does not expect to see such grace of movement, but one does.

As you watch a giraffe nibbling the top of a thorn tree, or bending his neck rather gawkily to reach a low bush, you may find it hard to believe that he has the same number of neck vertebrae as we have: seven. Each one is drawn out to a length of eight inches or more. This neck, together with the long legs, gives the animal his astonishing height.

Standing normally, a giraffe cannot get his lips down to water level at a stream or pool. He must bend his foreknees or straddle his front legs wide into a most uncomfortable-looking position. He can then just get his lips to water. With a sucking movement he pulls the water uphill, up the throat of that long neck and down to the stomach.

He adopts the same posture to get saline earth, but after filling his cheeks to the bulging point he quickly stands up, head high, to masticate the earth and swallow it. Strangely enough, he seems unable to spit out his mouthful; if attacked or chased he may choke, and seems to fall into a panic. African poachers take advantage of this to attack with poisoned arrows (the sound of a gunshot might bring park guards converging on the spot). Giraffe hide makes a good shield, and tail hairs fetch good prices to make bracelets for the tourist trade. Game-department officers collect tails from giraffes killed accidentally — for example, by trains — for the bracelet-weavers. I hope that a nylon substitute may come into use and save many a giraffe from poachers.

During the past few years the giraffe populations in Kenya and Tanzania seem to have increased. Men seldom shoot them for sport now, and giraffes have very few enemies except man. Lions do kill

Lone tusker stretches high to wrench a tangled branch from an acacia tree. Elephants can lay waste an entire woodland with their destructive feeding habits. They will push over trees and often only sample choice foliage or strips of bark before ambling on to others.

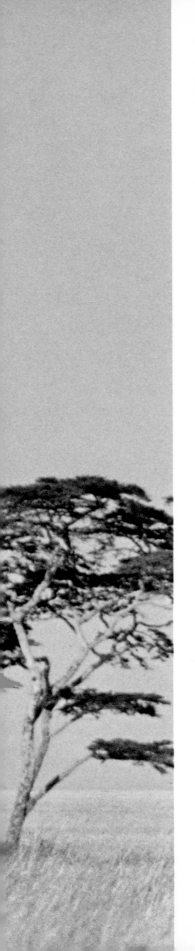

young ones; sometimes they even attack adults, but this entails a struggle and the lion may come off the worse—a giraffe's kick is very dangerous. Although a female may defend her calf, the parental bond is remarkably loose in this species. Offspring begin browsing in their first month and are rarely observed to suckle after they start eating leaves. Young giraffes sometimes leave their mothers' herd to join another for a time.

Adult herd structure seems even more casual—perhaps because the animals can keep up visual contact for about a mile. At Olduvai Gorge, our famous prehistoric site in Tanzania, we know a herd whose home range lies to the north. Its number has seldom varied above six or below four over the years. A much bigger herd lives to the south. Both resort to the bottom of the gorge for water when there is any, avoiding the steeper slopes. Neither ventures often into the area of the other group.

U NTIL RECENTLY books on Africa have suggested that there are several species of giraffe in different areas, basing the distinction largely on skin color and pattern. Now it is more usual to regard all giraffes as members of one species and the variants as members of geographic races, or subspecies. I am not sure, however, that even these are valid geographic races, since you can find examples of more than one supposed "race" in the same herd. Attempts have also been made in the past to classify giraffes by the number of "horns" the males carry, but one big herd can contain males with varying numbers and types.

True horns consist of a bony outgrowth of the skull covered with a sheath of keratin. Giraffe "horns" are bony bosses, covered with skin and a tuft of hair, and are not really horns at all. They may represent relics of pedicels from which antlers grew ages before, since giraffes are fairly closely related to deer.

In prehistoric times of higher rainfall, giraffes roamed the Sahara, and artists painted them from life on rocky bluffs miles from any water or vegetation today. This great strange animal seems to have attracted more notice from East African prehistoric artists than any other animal except possibly the eland; it figures very prominently indeed in rock paintings with colors still vivid.

Unlike the other giants of Africa, the giraffe always appears clean and tidy because it never resorts to mud baths, while both the elephant and rhino love mud wallows and dust baths.

My first encounter with a rhinoceros took place when I was not yet 15. A Kikuyu friend, Gichuru, had agreed to teach me the tribal techniques and rituals of beekeeping, and we were going to check on some hives near the eastern slopes of the Ngong Hills, about eight miles from my home. As usual for such a walk, he had his two-edged sword in its sheath of wood and goat leather. We were following a narrow path through high grass and bush when we heard a crashing noise on our right in thick cover. Gichuru drew his sword, and we waited. A bushpig? A bushbuck? Suddenly a rhino broke into view hardly four feet

Bull giraffes on the Serengeti shove with their hindquarters and swing their necks and heads like sledgehammers, landing blows sometimes audible half a mile away. The contest ends when one turns away. Giraffes inhabit much of the dry, lightly forested savanna of sub-Saharan Africa.

GEORGE B. SCHALLER, NEW YORK ZOOLOGICAL SOCIETY

Forelegs spread wide, a giraffe fills its mouth with saline earth to get the salt it needs. The animal leans down the same way to drink, sucking the water up its long throat, but when eating earth raises its head to chew and swallow.

BARON HUGO VAN LAWICK

away, and Gichuru hit it with the flat of his sword, hard, between eye and ear. The astonished animal made off in a hurry. At the time I thought we had been attacked, but looking back I think that the frightened creature simply rushed blindly toward an unrecognized sound.

This, of course, was the common "black rhino," *Diceros bicornis.* The "white rhino," *Ceratotherium simum,* has disappeared from East Africa except in northern Uganda. Their common names are most misleading, for both animals are gray—or soil-colored. Dutch colonists in South Africa called one rhino *wyd*, or wide, referring to its wide mouth and lips; this was corrupted in English to "white." I prefer to call this the "square-lipped rhino." Its square lips are particularly well adapted to grazing, although it can certainly browse to some extent. Standing five to six feet at the shoulder, with a massive hump at the nape, it will weigh more than two tons.

We know from subfossil bones that turn up in recent alluvial deposits, from prehistoric rock paintings, and from historical records that the square-lipped rhino was much more widespread during the past three to four thousand years until only a few centuries ago. Probably it has disappeared so rapidly because it is much more lethargic, mild-tempered, and easier to approach and kill than its smaller, prehensile-lipped cousin. In the 1890's my late uncle John Pigott shot one during an exploration trip up the Tana River; quite possibly, certainly unintentionally, he killed the last square-lipped rhino in Kenya.

Undoubtedly all the rhinos in Africa are in grave danger from poachers, because rhino horn commands a high price in the Far East, where it is rated as an aphrodisiac. Poachers consider the profit from one horn well worth the risk of a heavy fine or jail sentence or both. Traders from the coast pay the equivalent of $12 a pound, or sometimes more than $150 for a horn. Sold in powder form, such a horn eventually commands several thousand dollars in the Orient.

This "horn" is actually a dense mass of dermal filaments that grow from a bony base on the nasal bone, and I cannot help wondering whether science could not produce a substitute to capture the traffic and thus save the surviving rhinos from poachers.

Both types of rhinoceros are true surviving giants, present about two million years ago at sites like Olduvai and the Omo Valley in Ethiopia. From our Fort Ternan diggings, near Lake Victoria, we believe we have traced the ancestry of the black rhino back twelve million years.

Black rhinos remain widespread today, although never very numerous except where closely protected. They show great adaptability to different altitudes and habitats. They range from the coastal plain through sere bush country right up to mountain forests. They feed in open moorland on the highest slopes and seem equally adapted to the arid regions of northern Kenya. I once found one many miles from any shade or any apparent source of water, near Mount Kulal, feeding off succulents and other juicy plants.

The black rhino's triangular muzzle and moderately prehensile upper lip equip him well for browsing, but—contrary to some old reports —he is perfectly able to graze as well. During the wet season I have seen two black rhinos reveling in lush clover on the caldera floor at Ngorongoro, and they were reported to have remained there for five days.

Dropping cumbrously, a giraffe wrestles his heavy frame to the ground to chew the cud and rest. When recumbent a giraffe usually holds its head high to watch for predators.

For more than a decade conservationists have warned that the black rhino is in grave danger of extinction. My family and I have shared this view. Olduvai Gorge always has some resident rhinos, and we had reckoned their number at 13 to 15. During a spate of poaching we were distressed to find the skeletons of a dozen rhinos killed for their horns in a single year. Thereafter for some time we hardly saw a rhino, and feared that our population had been nearly exterminated.

Then, in 1964, a Canadian scientist, John Goddard, arrived to make careful studies. He devised a method of recording every rhino he saw by photographs in profile and full face, noting the shape of horns, the scars on ears, and the wrinkles on snouts. He built up a dossier and succeeded in identifying each member of a population. His count proved that more than 70 rhinos lived in a study area of 170 square miles centered on the gorge. This shows how difficult it can be to estimate animal populations accurately; aerial surveys gave much lower figures.

Goddard found that rhinos keep to a small home range—about 11 square miles in dry thornbush at Olduvai, 6 in the grassland of Ngorongoro, about 1 square mile in its lush Lerai Forest. These ranges may overlap. Males typically greet females with a pattern of behavior that includes a loud puffing snort; females approach one another warily, exchange gentle nudges with the sides of the head or joust briefly with anterior horns, and then one walks away. Neighbors normally tolerate each other. But if a stranger intrudes, the resident may become aggressive, especially if both are males. The resident attacks, screaming loudly; the intruder defends itself in silence until, typically, it flees, hotly pursued.

The black rhino may charge a man without warning, and in new settlement areas men kill the animals off as a precaution. Contrary to what many people claim, the rhino is not especially inclined to attack at sight. It sometimes attacks for lack of sight, as I know from experience.

Once at Olduvai, I took a student up the side gorge, where we hoped to see rhinos. Suddenly I said, "Mind, look out, Jean—there's a rhino coming!" Perhaps he had heard the sound of our footsteps. From the way he was holding his head low and his tail high, I thought he was in an uncertain temper. I helped Jean scramble up a nearby rock, about 10 feet high with good steep sides. The rhino came trotting on toward us. Suddenly, about 15 feet away, his little piggy eyes seemed to see us, or perhaps he caught our scent. At any rate he apparently recognized us as humans, for he turned and bolted away as fast as he could go.

I feel nearly certain that men often misinterpret a rhino's investigation of noise as an "unprovoked charge." While our young rhino turned and ran, an older animal might have reason to dislike man and press home a charge. Once, in self-defense, I shot a rhino that charged me from thick bush at point-blank range; I found an old, suppurating wound in his shoulder, apparently from a soft-nosed bullet.

Rhinos can be dangerous when they have their young with them, for they try very hard to protect their offspring. Adults have few enemies,

Overleaf: Revealing large razor-sharp tusks, a hippopotamus yawns in a threat display to warn away trespassers. The hippo remains in or near water during the day; at night the huge mammal leaves its pond or river to feed, consuming as much as 200 pounds of grass, herbs, and leaves on a single foray.

39

ALAN ROOT (ABOVE); CHRISTINA LOKE, PHOTO RESEARCHERS

but both lions and spotted hyenas may attack young ones. These predators are sufficiently quick of foot to run little risk that the parents will harm them. Nevertheless, Goddard saw a mother engage a rash young lion that charged her calf. The lion bit her leg and clawed her thigh, whereupon the rhino whirled and gored him twice in the ribs. She stabbed him in the neck as he rolled on the ground, and finished him off with a thrust at the base of the lower jaw.

In 1934 my wife Mary and I had a brush with rhinos while driving the rough earth track from Olduvai to Arusha in a small car. We saw a big bull rhino standing in the middle of the road ahead of us, so I stopped. We waited until he ambled off into the bush, and I started forward again, keeping an eye on the spot. We reached that point and saw not one adult but two, with a small calf. To my horror, both adults charged us. I accelerated to the best speed the car and the road would permit and started down the track at a dangerous pace. How far they followed I have no idea—both Mary and I had our eyes on the potholes and ruts ahead. Eventually, after breaking both back springs, we got away.

Although many and varied types of rhinos flourished in the past, and we know something about the ancestry of the African survivors, we know little, for certain, about the forebears of the strange animal that the ancient Greeks called *hippopotamos*, or "river horse." We do know that it is fairly closely related to the family of the pigs, and my colleague Shirley Coryndon is now studying fossils from early deposits in Kenya that may establish the true descent of the hippopotamus. The available specimens certainly suggest that at least some of the hippos of the past were every bit as much aquatic animals as the present-day species.

Except for occasional periods of sunbathing and drowsing on mudbanks or sandbars, or wallowing in mud, hippos spend the day in the water. Occasionally they submerge completely, rising every three to four minutes for breath. They may nibble a little on water plants in the shallows, but during the day they do not really engage in feeding. At night they move onto land and wander for several miles in search of grazing—perhaps 200 pounds of grass per adult.

Since the hippo spends the night away from the protection of the water, getting food to satisfy the needs of his huge body, he evidently does not lie down to rest or sleep. I doubt that anyone knows whether his daytime repose in the water is sleep or mere drowsing. One might wonder if he dozes during his brief periods under water. This raises a most interesting problem regarding sleep among wild animals and the extent of sleep—in the human sense, as distinct from rest and repose—that is necessary to various species.

Lions certainly sleep by day, mostly in "cat winks." They sprawl fully relaxed, with eyes closed, but they can spring into fully alert wakefulness in the twinkling of an eye. It is uncertain whether elephants in the wild regularly sleep by night, although in zoos and circuses they do so for several hours at a time. In the wild I have seen them resting by day, either just standing up or leaning against a large tree. Some observers

Blimp-like hippos laze in a muddy wallow in Queen Elizabeth National Park, Uganda, as cattle egrets search for insects stirred up by the animals. At left, hippos slash at each other in a fight that lasted for an hour and left one with deep, bleeding wounds.

Overleaf: Herd of Cape buffalo stampedes through red oat grass in the Great Rift Valley. Normally peaceful grazers, these massive animals fight viciously when attacked by lion or man—their principal enemies.

HELEN AND FRANK SCHREIDER, NATIONAL GEOGRAPHIC STAFF

have photographed them lying on their sides, eyes closed, trunks curled in a spiral—and have even heard them snoring. Giraffe and many of the antelopes spend the daylight hours either feeding or lying down chewing the cud and also, apparently, do the same throughout the night. They may put their heads down and shut their eyes for two to five minutes several times during the day and night, but I do not think they sleep deeply. Rhinos, on the other hand, do sleep, usually by day, lying on their stomachs with legs tucked under them, but I have also seen them flat out on their sides, sleeping so soundly that twice I have been deceived into thinking I had found a dead one!

What do these phenomena mean? Perhaps man and other animals that sleep deeply and at some length have developed the habit because they have little to fear during extended unconsciousness. Man can assure himself of a high degree of safety; lions and rhinos have no natural enemy except man. In contrast, creatures like giraffes and antelopes must stay ever on the alert for danger from predators. Also, it may be that their digestive systems require them to chew the cud almost continuously when they are not feeding. So perhaps the equivalent of sleep in many animals is rest and repose. Here, I feel, is a wonderful project for a study in depth. In the past decade we have learned a great deal about the complexities of human sleep. Now we need to know more about animal sleep and sleepless repose.

Cattle egret perches on the back of a Cape buffalo on the shore of Lake Manyara, Tanzania. When alarmed, egrets flap noisily away, alerting their hosts to possible danger. Shoulder-deep in mud, the buffalo at right escapes the heat by lounging in a wallow.

R ESEARCH on hippopotamus behavior and ecology became an urgent matter for the Uganda parks authorities by 1956. In Queen Elizabeth National Park, the Kazinga Channel between Lakes Edward and George provides a permanent waterway, and here the hippo population increased excessively. Ranging farther and farther inland, the animals turned grassland into stretches of barren dust and mud. Planned culling of as many as 1,000 hippos a year seemed to bring the population in balance with food supply.

In other regions hippos may find their watery home drying up under especially severe drought conditions. Then, unless they can travel to some other lake or river, their skin blisters badly with sunburn, their food supply fails, and they perish in great numbers. I remember when the shallow waters of Lake Rukwa in southwestern Tanzania dried up, and hundreds of these poor creatures died. Perhaps this is nature's way of keeping down their numbers, for hippos run few risks except that of being shot for meat or a lion's attack on the young.

Female hippos use shallow water as a nursery for their young. At Mzima Springs in Tsavo National Park you can stand on a small pier to look down into the clear water at mothers and their little ones, as well as big adult males. Sometimes they rise quietly for air; mostly only the top of the head clears the surface, a rapid waggling of ears sends two small showers sparkling, and the animal slips under again in a circle of shimmering ripples. Sometimes they surge up noisily, grunting and yawning. One utters a loud *unnnk;* another answers from the bulrush clumps at the far end of the pool.

We tend to think of hippos as fat and cumbersome, with their stubby legs, low-slung bellies, and ungainliness on land. But much of their bulk is pure muscle, biologists have found, and they can outpace a man when

aroused. The transformation when they enter the water must be seen to be believed. They get about with a slow gliding movement so well coordinated it is almost a poem, and I find it close to impossible to bring myself away.

On the other hand, when you watch buffalo from a car in a national park, you recognize at once the familiar behavior of domestic cattle. They graze unconcernedly in herds of fifty or a hundred or even more, or lie peacefully in patches of shade to chew the cud. Indeed, it seems very odd to me that few serious attempts have been made to domesticate the African species. Its adaptability, from sea level to mountain forests, and its relative immunity to some of the cattle diseases would seem to make it an ideal animal for ranching. A good bull, standing 5 feet at the shoulder, may weigh more than a ton. Peoples like the Kikuyu, who regarded game animals as unfit for food and taboo, treated buffalo flesh as legitimate meat, on a par with beef. They tanned the skins, thick and tough but workable as elephant and rhino hide are not, for the best possible war shields. In my boyhood I learned the Kikuyu practice of trapping buffalo in deep game pits near a watering pool, a swamp, or a lakeshore. Although lions will attack a buffalo, they sometimes come off very badly when other members of the herd retaliate. I have seen at least one record of hyenas killing a young calf, but buffalo hold their own against most predators.

Hunters often call buffalo the most dangerous of all African big game. It is not an easy animal to kill outright. The massive horns protect the brain from front and side. A heart shot is difficult, and a shot through the lungs that will drop almost any other animal leaves a buffalo capable of doing a lot of damage before he succumbs. I believe, in fact, that a wounded buffalo is the most cunning and most dangerous of all the animals I know. As soon as you wound him, he is liable to be stalking you as much as you are stalking him. I have lost three friends killed when trying to follow up wounded bulls. Each had gone on alone—it is understood among hunters that you do not take anyone else into danger if you can avoid it. The buffalo—like the great predators, like the other surviving giants—commands man's respect.

Disturbed and puzzled, a black rhinoceros (opposite), purses the prehensile upper lip used in pulling leaves and twigs from low trees and bushes. At left, a white rhino, a larger, more placid beast, forages with a square lip adapted to grazing. White rhinos gather in family groups of up to seven members; black rhinos frequently lead solitary lives.

BARON HUGO VAN LAWICK (LEFT); M. P. KAHL

3

Predators Great and Small

You don't turn your back on His Majesty. That's the best advice I can offer if you're on foot in Africa and you encounter a lion. In the parks, of course, you usually stay in your vehicle; and outside the parks you're unlikely to meet big game at close quarters. Until our first season at Olduvai, in 1931-32, my experiences with lions had been very limited. Then, at Olduvai and at Apis Rock, a Stone Age site some 25 miles north of the gorge, lions became almost a part of our day-to-day life and I could study them at firsthand.

I have no doubt at all, now, that lions are not normally hostile to man or interested in man as an item of food, but they are insatiably curious about any unusual occurrence.

When we put up camp at Olduvai, on the first night and for many nights thereafter, lions came round the tents soon after dark to investigate us. Travelers in those days usually surrounded their camp with a thornbush fence to keep out lions. Our neighbors made no attempt to attack us, though we had no fence and slept with the tent flaps open, but only after several weeks did they begin to accept our presence and stop coming around.

We camped at the end of the season beside a rather dirty little water hole called Len Lemoru, between Loliondo and Olduvai, and an incident occurred there that clearly showed the lions' inquisitive nature. After an early supper we lay down next to the trucks to sleep. One of the men, Ndekei, had been running a temperature and, feeling rather shivery, he decided to curl up in his blanket by the supper fire, some 20 yards from the rest of us. During the night I woke up to hear hand-clapping and a man calling "Shoo! Shoo! Shoo!" "What's the matter?" I asked loudly. Ndekei replied, in a voice muffled by the blanket, that he had driven off some animal that had come and sniffed at his head—a jackal, he thought. I jumped up and switched on the spotlight of my lorry. There by the water, just 25 yards away, stood seven magnificent lions!

I warned everyone to keep quite still, and stood by with a rifle in case anything happened. As I expected, the lions finished their drink and after about 20 minutes moved on out of sight. By that time most of the party had gone to sleep again. Ndekei, I must say, had been a bit surprised. Had he panicked and tried to run, the lions would almost certainly have struck him down.

A dying fire, as this incident suggests, does not keep off prowling lions, and they will freely enter a safari camp lighted by a portable generator. Apparently, however, they dislike smoke. I have even been assured that the smell of a good strong cigar—if the wind is right—will send lions off very quickly indeed.

I remember from boyhood how African friends, as well as European hunters, used to recommend climbing trees if in danger from a lion, in the wholly false belief that the animal could not follow. Lions in fact climb quite well, though not so well as leopards. This fallacy may have arisen because in some regions, such as around Nairobi, we have no record of tree climbing by lions; in other places, however, notably Queen Elizabeth National Park in Uganda and Lake Manyara National Park in Tanzania, lions climb trees regularly.

In the parks today visitors concentrate on getting as close to lions as possible. Once in a great while an edgy lioness may approach growling,

Majestic symbol of Africa and the continent's mightiest predator, the lion strikes down zebra, buffalo, and antelopes of all sizes, but gets part of its food by eating carrion and robbing smaller predators. Lionesses do most of the hunting, often killing prey by biting deeply into the throat.

ears flattened and tail lashing, to warn intruders away from her cubs, but as a rule lions regard cars with great indifference. You can sit in a Land-Rover and watch a mother licking a small cub so energetically that she pushes him right over her own strong foreleg, or a cub trying his skill with a grass stem. He holds it down with his left paw, bites it fiercely, twists his head sharply, finds the stem too tough to break, and turns to a litter-mate; they begin wrestling, each with a forepaw on the other's shoulder. Toward sunset you may see lions on their way to water, adults strolling soberly while nearly grown youngsters play a kind of follow-the-leader, rushing in turn up a slanting tree trunk and whirling to jump down again. From midmorning to late afternoon you can expect to find lions sprawled in the best shade available. Even when they bother to open their eyes they give you at best a lazy glance.

Other cats have, in general, the reputation of leading relatively solitary lives. Typically, the largest group is a mother (with or without a male in attendance) and her cubs. Lions, however, stand out as truly gregarious. One does come across solitary lions, but it is far more common to find them in a party, or pride, of four to as many as thirty.

GEORGE B. SCHALLER, NEW YORK ZOOLOGICAL SOCIETY

In an attack that nearly failed, a lioness hangs from the neck of a screaming zebra (opposite, above) after pouncing onto its side and losing her grip. Grappling clumsily with her prey (above), she finally pulls it to earth, almost on top of her. At the approach of another lioness, she released the zebra, and the terrified creature bolted toward a nearby riverbank with the two cats close behind (left). After a chase of some 60 feet the predators overtook and killed their quarry. Lions adapt hunting tactics to the situation, sometimes waiting in ambush, at other times stalking through tall grass to within a few feet of grazing animals before springing. A hunt by several working together in open terrain often ends in a kill, possibly explaining why lions have become the most gregarious of the cats, living in prides numbering as many as 30 animals.

The first intensive long-term study of lion behavior began in 1966 when Dr. George B. Schaller, with the support of the National Science Foundation and the New York Zoological Society, and photographic assistance from the National Geographic Society, initiated a three-year investigation of the lions of the Serengeti National Park. Schaller has followed them in a Land-Rover by day and by night, collecting data on their food habits, movements, and social behavior.

He has reported that members of a pride will leave their fellows to roam apart, sometimes for days, but hardly ever leave their own territory—an area that varies with the density of prey. Lions mark a territory in a number of ways—roaring is one, spraying bushes with strongly scented urine is another—and strangers rarely intrude. A pride male may welcome a strange female, but the females will try to oust her. They in turn might mate with a strange male, but the males will attempt to drive him off.

Fights over territory seldom occur. When a strange male intrudes upon the holding of a pride, one of the resident males may charge him and chase him for two miles or more but will rarely catch him. Indeed the pursuing male seems deliberately to avoid overtaking the stranger. He apparently adjusts his speed to match that of the fleeing lion, roaring fiercely all the while. In one case, however, a male died of his wounds after a battle with three others.

A lioness gives birth to as many as six cubs—though the normal litter is two to four—at intervals of some 20 months, and people often ask me what keeps the lion population within reasonable bounds. Modern studies indicate that a very high proportion of the cubs never reaches maturity. A few succumb to accidents; endemic diseases kill many; others, born weak, get insufficient food to survive.

Given a choice, lions prefer the larger prey—wildebeest, zebra, hartebeest, topi—but they eat whatever is most readily available and commonly will kill and eat warthog, impala, and gazelle. They also like to take a domestic ox or cow for a change, and sometimes eat guinea fowl or small game. Surprising as it may seem, they have no objection to carrion, and will gorge themselves on a kill made by other predators.

Because the press always gives a lot of publicity to cases of man-eating, the impression survives that lions normally kill human beings for food. Comparatively few actually turn man-eater, and I believe these are abnormal: old and decrepit, or sick, wounded, or injured, or living in areas where man has killed off their natural prey.

The classic case of man-eating occurred at Tsavo in present-day Kenya just before the turn of the century. The strange and terrifying tale is recorded in a book, *The Man-Eaters of Tsavo*, written by Lt. Col. J. H. Patterson, the British engineer who eventually killed the two lions involved. Colonel Patterson had been placed in charge of a section of railway being built from the coast inland to the northeastern shore of Lake Victoria through what was then the British East Africa Protectorate. His specific task was to construct a 60-mile segment of the line that would include a bridge across the Tsavo River.

Mysteriously, soon after Patterson's arrival at Tsavo, railway workers began to disappear. At first Patterson would not credit stories that lions

Capable of consuming 75 pounds of meat and hide in a day, a big male gorges on wildebeest—he may not eat again for several days. Pride members often fight vigorously over a large kill; if game becomes scarce some cubs will starve. Below, a tawny lioness, sated with meat, drinks from a shadowed pool in the Seronera River.

Sprawled in a thin line of shade, a pride on the Serengeti rests through the heat of the day. Most indolent of the big cats, well-fed lions may rest and doze 20 hours out of 24, hunting in early morning and evening. In areas where man has made them wary, they hunt mainly at night. Always unpredictable and potentially dangerous, they become especially aggressive when hungry. Catnap over, the lion above awakens with a wide yawn.

had devoured them. Nonetheless, the man-eaters had begun to strike. They harried the construction crews for nine months, invading thorn-fenced enclosures by night and dragging away their screaming victims.

Somehow the pair had acquired a taste for human flesh. Possibly they had first killed a worker and tasted his blood after jumping into an enclosure in search of donkey flesh, relished by lions fully as much as zebra meat. Also, their normal prey was undoubtedly reduced by the presence of thousands of railway workers and by the shooting of the area's game for food and trophies.

Patterson hunted the lions, set traps for them, and frequently waited in trees where he thought them likely to appear, but they consistently eluded him. They attacked at first one and then another of the workers' camps, which were scattered across several miles in country covered with stunted trees and thick underbrush.

During December of 1898 the lions' forays became so determined that they brought about what Patterson described as "a perfect reign of terror," completely halting work on the railway for some three weeks. In satisfying their new appetite for human flesh the lions pushed through thornbush fences as strong as the men could construct, and ignored firebrands, shouts, and even gunshots. Scores of Indian and African workers fell victim to the man-eaters before Patterson finally succeeded in shooting them.

Man is certainly the lion's greatest enemy. Within historic times the lion's range has shrunk from the Balkans, the Near East, and North Africa, to Africa south of the Sahara, with a small population of Indian lions remaining in the Gir Forest. Outside park areas, men still hunt them with high-powered rifles, calling it sport, while herd-owners kill lions to protect domestic stock.

Lions seldom kill for the fun of it, but I heard of an incident near our home at Langata, outside Nairobi, when a lion supposedly got into a pen of turkeys one night and killed them all, one by one, striking them on the head with a forepaw. If this was true it was unusual to a degree, and I have never been convinced that the culprit was not a huge leopard, since the identification was based only on pawprints.

L EOPARDS may live, unsuspected, quite close to human settlements. Elusive, nocturnal, and in the main silent, these richly spotted cats remain the least-known of Africa's famous game. As a rule the leopard prowls unseen — until he decides otherwise.

Not long after Father refused to let us keep "our" cubs, we went to stay with friends of my parents on the outskirts of Nairobi, not far from where the Anglican Cathedral now stands. The grown-ups were having dinner in another part of the bungalow, and my sisters and I had gone to bed. Suddenly we saw a leopard spring through one of the open windows of our bedroom, a dark shape against the night sky. Then, sensing the presence of humans, it took fright and hid under my elder

Overleaf: Curious three-month-old cubs and a lioness take the late-afternoon sun on the ledges of a kopje, or granite outcrop, a favored resting place of lions. Females normally bear two to four cubs every 20 months or so. As male cubs reach maturity older males usually drive them from the pride.

JOAN AND ALAN ROOT

57

sister's bed. We did not dare to call out for fear of provoking the leopard to attack. We did not even whisper. The leopard stayed perfectly silent too. After a time it went out the way it had come in.

The boldness and wariness of that animal are supremely characteristic of leopards in any part of their wide range, from coastal forests to high in the mountains. They vary, however, in both size and color, and some writers on East Africa distinguish the so-called desert leopard from the bush leopard and the forest leopard. All three belong to the same species but have adapted to different habitats. Forest leopards may reach a length of 8 feet or more from nose to tail tip and stand 2½ feet high at the shoulder—very big indeed; often the ground tone of their coats is a rich chestnut. Bush leopards are intermediate in size and color. In the northern arid regions leopards run very small—barely half as big as the forest strain—and very pale in color. A friend of mine long ago brought a "desert" cub to his farm near Mount Kenya, where with plentiful food and a cooler climate it grew as large as a forest leopard. As far as I remember, it retained its light-hued coat.

Today leopard skin sells at high prices for ladies' handbags and coats, and many poachers think it well worth their while to trap or shoot the animals illegally and sell the pelts on the black market. I can see no valid reason for the slaughter of such a beautiful animal in the wild. If women really feel they want these furs, then let someone set up leopard farms and breed leopards for the purpose, as has been done with silver foxes. That, at least, would help to check the destruction of the ever-diminishing wild stock.

Although the law affords leopards strict protection, it allows the defense of livestock such as sheep and goats. If a man trying to sell the skin of an illegally killed leopard claims he shot the animal when it entered his sheep pen, it's not easy to disprove the story. Luckily farmers are beginning to take an interest in preserving leopards, and an increasing number of them follow the practice of trapping the animals in box traps and releasing them in a far-away park.

In some park areas it is gradually becoming possible to see leopards in broad daylight. Around Seronera Lodge in the Serengeti they have come to realize that man—or at least man in a car—is not an enemy. There, driving slowly along the rivers with their screens of acacia trees and thornbush, you may even pull up beside a leopard resting on the ground at the edge of a thicket. But if other cars approach, the animal may grow restless, green eyes staring alertly, tail rippling uneasily—and suddenly the leopard flashes across open ground to the protection of a tree or the cover of thick bush.

Leopards spend much time in trees, resting on a big horizontal branch in the heat of the day. Also, they often take prey into a tree to keep it safe from hyenas and jackals. Vultures, apparently from fear of the cats, rarely touch a leopard's kill, even when it is left unguarded. If you see the remains of a gazelle or a wildebeest calf draped in the fork of a tree, the leopard is probably not far away.

Twice I have found leopards feeding on a dead rhinoceros some 24 hours after the animal was shot, when it had begun to decompose; and they may return to a kill for several consecutive days.

Unfortunately, leopards are notoriously fond of dog flesh. Once a

Young bat-eared fox sniffs expectantly at a parent's muzzle to learn if it has brought food. Diminutive carnivores, they hunt insects and small rodents and raid ground birds' nests for eggs and nestlings. Parents summon the young with a whistling call.

colleague of mine and his wife were sitting in their home near Nairobi when a leopard jumped right in through a window, grabbed their pet dog, and jumped out again. Such episodes are far from rare in leopard country, usually taking place around dusk.

... are fond of baboon and of wild pig, and in farm a... ...een greatly reduced in number these crea-t... ...o crops that the government has to send in te... ...h traps and rifles.

...ation of being more dangerous to man than any other African carnivore—it can hide itself easily, attacks with great speed, and offers a small, difficult target. Friends of mine both white and black have been mauled by leopards over the years, but none—luckily—was killed. African leopards occasionally turn man-eater, but none has claimed as many recorded victims as the famous man-eaters of India.

A LUCKY PHOTOGRAPHER in Kenya filmed the most remarkable leopard episode I've ever seen. Two spotted hyenas attacked three leopard cubs. The parents rushed back as soon as the cubs began to squeal, and defended their offspring in the most tremendous fight I ever saw, with honors more or less even. When the hyenas eventually ran away, all the adults were wounded but the cubs were safe.

If our knowledge of leopards is far from adequate, we know even less about the habits of the smaller cats, especially the African wildcat, *Felis libyca*. A little larger than the average domestic cat, it looks rather like a familiar "tabby" with a thick, usually ringed, tail. I can be reasonably sure of seeing a wildcat in the car headlights if I drive across the plains near Olduvai to a colony of *Pedetes*, or spring hares. After eight or nine in the evening these rodents emerge from their burrows, and the wildcat seems to prefer them for food when he can catch them. Otherwise I have only seen it on rare occasions. If you locate an area where a pair has a family, you may see them out hunting for birds and rodents by daylight to keep a hungry litter of kittens in food.

Their range extends over much of Africa, and they represent the stock from which the familiar Abyssinian domestic race is derived. In settled areas they will mate with domestic cats, but I've never known one successfully tamed—those I've seen were spitfires to the end.

For some reason the medium-size cats, the caracal and the serval, are not quite so intractable. If caught young, caracal tame easily; my son Jonathan has two that roam near and through the house, and are fond of sitting on bookcases and willing to feed from his hand.

They prey on birds and rodents, but they will also tackle young gazelles. According to the Masai, they take a lamb or kid from the herds now and then.

The caracal's close relationship to the European lynx is obvious in the contour of body and the black tufts on the pointed ears. Although the short fur ranges from dark chestnut to light fawn, depending on their geographical range, caracals always have off-white bellies with shadow spotting—and are always very handsome.

I have only seen caracals in the wild about half a dozen times in all my life in East Africa, not because they are rare but because they are mainly nocturnal. Mary and I know that one pair lives near the digging

M. P. KAHL

Enormous, acutely sensitive ears of the bat-eared fox can detect the faint underground scratchings of feeding dung-beetle larvae. To reach the grubs—buried by the adult beetles—he digs up and cracks open the earth-caked balls of dung that shelter them.

Wildebeest calf stands rigid in shock as Cape hunting dogs tear at its flesh. Packs ranging from 3 or 4 dogs to as many as 25 prey on wildebeest, gazelle, and other plains game. Some experts call wild dogs Africa's most efficient predators; they race after prey at 35 miles an hour and catch what they pursue in three of four attempts. When the pack has pups still in the dens, hunters regurgitate food for them and their adult guardians, as well as for any other dogs that remain behind. At right, a pack moves across the Serengeti in search of quarry.

BARON HUGO VAN LAWICK (ABOVE); GEORGE B. SCHALLER, NEW YORK ZOOLOGICAL SOCIETY

site at Olduvai that we designate as TK, and another up the side gorge near site SHK, but I've only seen each of these pairs once. Their tracks, however, make it clear that they are around all the time. Twice I've had a glimpse of young kittens, once near Olduvai and once by the road from Nairobi to the Olorgesailie [Ololkisalie] prehistoric site. On both occasions the parents took them off very quickly into a dense thicket.

Today the caracal is still fairly common in parts of Israel, one of a number of animals that provide a faunal link between Africa and the Near East. In marked contrast, the serval is confined to Africa. About the height of the caracal, some 20 inches at the shoulder, the serval is unmistakably different, with large upright oval ears, a leggy build, and a rich tawny-yellow coat marked with large black spots.

SERVALS NORMALLY HUNT by night, but on rare occasions you may see one out in full daylight, and then you can be almost certain there's a litter not far away. In this sort of situation it really pays the photographer to be very patient. If you are lucky you will see one of the parents pounce into a tuft of grass for a mouse, or stalk and kill a hare, and carry its prey to a patch of low bush. There it will make a soft purring noise just like a domestic cat, and out into the open will come two or three serval kittens. If you have a telephoto lens (because you certainly won't get very close), you will get charming pictures of mother and infants chasing each other and playing and having mock fights.

Poultry owners trap servals ruthlessly, since these cats like a meal of fat fowl or duck, but the greatest threat to the serval today comes from the fact that its fur resembles that of cheetah closely enough that it can be sold to the unsuspecting—along with cheetah pelts—as "leopard skin." I fear that this trend may endanger the species.

Before World War I, every Kikuyu youth had to complete his regalia for the final pre-initiation dance with a serval pelt hanging from the back of the waist to the knee, its forelegs forming a kind of belt. A lucky boy might borrow one from a father who had carefully saved the skin he had worn, or from an elder brother, but most youths spent weeks before the rite trying to hunt or trap a *kirume*. This name means "stunted"— the tribe thought of the serval as a variety of the much larger cheetah that somehow became permanently stunted in youth.

An adult cheetah stands 2½ to 3 feet at the shoulder, with a body length about the same as a forest leopard's, but out on the open plains it seems able to melt into nothing. I was driving near Olduvai a few years ago with some members of the National Geographic Society's Committee for Research and Exploration. The twitch of a black-banded ear caught my eye. I stopped the Land-Rover and said, pointing, "There's a cheetah over there."

My companions could see nothing, for the animal was lying flat in a slight depression made by generations of game going to water. Had the ear not moved I might have missed it, but I knew from long experience that the flicker meant only one thing—cheetah. I drove up very slowly to within 25 feet; after a time the cheetah decided we were too close for comfort and trotted away.

At full speed over short distances the cheetah is the world's fastest land mammal, but to catch a gazelle or an impala he must start his

Vigilant spotted hyena drinks from the Munge
River in Ngorongoro Crater. The animals watch
for fish in such shallow drinking places, occasionally
scooping one out with a flashing front paw. Females
generally weigh more than their mates and sometimes
dominate the clans. They guard their offspring fiercely,
at times from cannibalistic fathers. At left, a mother
nurses her young as another adult rests nearby.

attacking rush from reasonably close—100 yards or less—for the great burst of speed tires him quickly.

Cape hunting dogs as well as cheetah often use what I call "the diagonal open approach." In effect this means that the animal being stalked sees the approaching enemy for a long time only in profile. I have concluded that many animals do not regard a carnivore as a threat when they can see it in profile. I've seen cheetah and wild dog move to within striking distance of gazelle this way. Then suddenly they turn toward the selected victim and charge. At this moment the animal realizes its danger, but often too late.

I MYSELF LEARNED to use this visible, slow, diagonal approach from Joshua. The essential thing, he said, was not to look as though bent upon attack. Don't show the hands or arms at all. If possible break your shape a little by tying some leaves across the middle of the body—gazelles and antelopes regularly flee from recognized danger, but less often from an object they do not understand, and about which they become curious.

The cheetah's shape is distinctive: small head, long legs, lanky body, the most sway-backed animal I know. Because it cannot sheath or fully retract its claws like most other cats, and for other less obvious reasons, zoologists put the cheetah in a genus of its own, *Acinonyx*.

We still know far too little about these beautiful beasts. They seem to migrate, at least to a local extent. At times we have several pairs not far from camp at Olduvai; at other times they all disappear. Mortality among the cubs is high. You see a mother with three or four cubs, and a few weeks later she may have only one or two left. Yet I know of cheetah that have safely brought up four cubs. Whether the chief cause of death is disease or some predator, such as the spotted hyena, I do not know. Once I saw a large martial eagle swoop at a cub hardly bigger than a small terrier. The parents had no chance to protect it—the eagle attacks so swiftly there's no question of defense, but that time the cub escaped.

A human may capture young cheetah fairly easily. The cubs cower and the mother runs—I've never heard of a female attacking in this situation. Indeed, wild cheetah seem very afraid of man, although they tame easily. Indian princes once used them to hunt gazelle.

Cheetah in the wild like very fresh meat of their own killing. I've never seen one touch carrion, nor do I know of a cheetah returning to its own kill for a second meal. It may not even succeed in finishing the first. I have watched cheetah driven off their kill by spotted hyenas, even by vultures.

Unaggressive and mild-tempered, these creatures are in real danger. A very few survive in Asia, but their range has shrunk. The fur trade wants their skins for handbags, gloves, and coats. Living on the open plains, cheetah are much easier to find and kill than leopard. In theory

Spotted hyenas attack zebra in Ngorongoro Crater, belying their reputation as cowardly scavengers. A mare (center) became separated after a stallion dropped back to defend the herd, then fell to the pack (lower). The hyenas' eyes reflect the camera's flash. A pair of jackals await their chance at the carcass.

BARON HUGO VAN LAWICK

the law gives them complete protection throughout East Africa—but the law is not always effective.

Smaller predators may fare better, the genet and the palm civet, or "Nandi tree cat," for example. Genets are lithe, long-bodied animals that seem particularly fond of associating with man, or at least of being near him, without being tamed at all. When I was young wild genets took up residence with us on two occasions. One pair lived in the thatch roof of our house; later another pair occupied a high shelf in my father's carpentry shop and slept there happily by day. They never came down when our dogs were around, but they did not really seem afraid of us. Years later, at Olduvai, genets of a different, dry-country species made their home with Mary and me in our camp. A single male came first—eventually he was joined by a female—and in the evenings he would come quite close to us and wait to be given tidbits. Sometimes he would even do this by day.

I cannot imagine how the Nandi tree cat ever got the name of "palm civet." To me it is more catlike than the civets, for it climbs well and has retractile claws and a mewing voice. In the main it is arboreal and nocturnal. It inhabits the forests, from the coastal plain to quite high altitudes, as on Mount Kenya. Only twice have I seen one in the wild, curled up on the branch of a tree for the day, close to the trunk. Probably, however, it is not so rare as this suggests.

While genets prey on birds, frogs, rats, mice, and insects, the Nandi tree cat seems to prefer fruit. It will also take insects and an occasional small bird, and birds' eggs.

These creatures make most interesting but not affectionate pets. My son Richard and his wife Margaret had a Nandi tree cat for a time, and we often admired its acrobatics. The Nandi tree cat will climb a straight pole with a kind of looping motion I have never seen in any other animal. The forelegs reach up and take a firm grip; then the hind legs are brought up like the legs of a man climbing a rope; then the forelegs move up again. Genets on the other hand display the skill they use to cross from one tree to another in the forest, moving swiftly along a horizontal liana. I have seen one cross a yard, balancing on a rather slack clothesline, a most impressive feat.

THE TRUE CIVET is a terrestrial animal about 3½ feet long, including the 15-to-18-inch tail; it weighs as much as 40 pounds, and has non-retractile claws like a dog's. When it comes out just before dusk for its nocturnal forays, you may be able to see the dark blotches and bars on its deep-gray sides as clearly as the black markings that cover the eyes and cheeks, and the white of the muzzle and ear tips. I've seen them on rare occasions among sansevieria thickets at Olduvai, and smelled the strong scent they expel from their anal glands to repel enemies.

Civets are common in highland areas of Kenya and Tanzania. They have a bad name for raiding poultry runs, but as far as I can tell—having studied their dung when I could since my boyhood—they prefer insects and centipedes, with occasional frogs, toads, and lizards. Once, near Lindi on the south Tanzanian coast, I met a civet on the beach just before twilight—he was moving along slowly, looking for an easy meal of crabs as the tide went out.

Scavenging black-backed jackals (below) devour the carcass of a wildebeest. Jackals often remain hidden in brush or in their dens through the day, emerging at dusk to clean up carrion left by predators. Occasionally they feed on fruit, insects, small mammals, reptiles, and birds, and sometimes kill unguarded gazelle fawns. At right, pups wait for their parents to bring food.

BARON HUGO VAN LAWICK (ABOVE); GEORGE B. SCHALLER, NEW YORK ZOOLOGICAL SOCIETY

Nocturnal prowlers: Stealthy genet (above) freezes before pouncing on its prey —a hare, bird, or perhaps a lizard. The arboreal palm civet, or "Nandi tree cat," (lower left) seldom emerges during the day. A serval (lower right) devours a yellow-necked francolin. At night it often raids poultry yards.

ALAN ROOT

I have never seen a photograph of a true civet in its natural habitat, or even heard of one. The person who takes one will have a real trophy!

On the other hand, innumerable photographers have caught the unmistakable figure of the spotted hyena, with its sloping back and rough coat, its deep-muzzled head and sidelong stare. An equally familiar reputation — that of a scavenging coward — clings to both the spotted hyena, *Crocuta crocuta*, and its smaller, striped cousin, *Hyaena hyaena*.

My African friends of boyhood days had no such misguided ideas about the spotted hyena. They considered it fully capable of killing sheep, goats, and cattle, and not unwilling to attack man.

Three incidents made me realize that spotted hyenas can be dangerous. A Miss Collyer, on a farm about a mile from our home at Kabete, left some young steers in a paddock at night, because there were no lions around. One morning she found two of her best animals dead and partly devoured. At first she was most unwilling to believe this was the work of hyenas, but the tracks were clearly visible.

Similarly, a farmer at Nanyuki, near the slopes of Mount Kenya, lost a number of oxen to a pack of hungry hyenas that attacked and killed by day. In the third instance a young girl was brought to my father one night for emergency treatment — she had strayed outside the family hut after dark, and a spotted hyena had attacked her and bitten a large piece of flesh from her buttocks.

In the ordinary course of events neither species of hyena ventures very close to man by day, but I had a thoroughly unpleasant experience after dark with a pack of spotted hyenas during our first season at Olduvai. Some of us had gone out in our truck to get meat, for in those days we had to rely a great deal on what we could shoot for fresh food. We had bagged a hartebeest and were returning, late in the evening, when the clutch gave up and we came to an abrupt stop. I sent two men ahead with our only lantern to walk the six miles to the camp and send spare clutch plates back the next morning.

We had broken down in the open, on the plains east of the gorge, but Ndekei and I managed to collect a few dry twigs, light a small fire, and grill some of the hartebeest meat. We were just thinking of settling down to sleep when I became aware of stealthy movements in the darkness around us. There was no moon, but in the starlight we could just make out a dozen or more dark shapes. As they got nearer we realized that spotted hyenas were moving in on us. Obviously the scent of meat had attracted them.

I did not like this situation very much. After a short time I got out my rifle and gave Ndekei my shotgun. We shouted at the animals, but they seemed determined to come on at us. Quite suddenly, with an outburst of growls and howls, the whole pack charged at once. "Shoot! Shoot!" I called as I fired. Two hyenas fell, and the rest rushed upon them and dragged them off.

For the rest of the night the pack left us alone. We found in the morning that the hyenas had devoured their own dead.

This incident, and those of my boyhood days, taken together with a recent field study conducted by a young Dutch scientist, Dr. Hans Kruuk, show how wrong is the widespread belief that spotted hyenas are nothing but cowardly scavengers. Actually their own kills are sometimes scavenged by lions, and they have even been known to attack and drive the big cats away from their feast.

I have concluded that the myth of the spotted hyena's cowardice arose from a confusion between it and the striped hyena. The latter's range extends through North Africa and India, where Europeans formed their impressions of hyenas—and the striped hyena is fundamentally a scavenger (although it will kill small creatures like dik-dik on its own account). So far as I know, there is no record of a striped hyena hunting or killing any large animals, and it certainly seems exceedingly frightened of man.

An even stranger myth still prevails among Europeans and Africans: that all spotted hyenas are hermaphrodites. This is utterly untrue; but the external sex organs of the female *Crocuta* do bear a resemblance to those of the male. Consequently a hunter who shoots what he believes to be a male, and then finds that the creature was pregnant or lactating, may believe that he has confirmed the old story.

REPORTS about the strength of a spotted hyena's jaws, however strange, are in my opinion unquestionably true. This hyena can and does crunch up and swallow much of the bone from large animals, to be dissolved almost completely in the digestive tract.

The spotted hyena lives mainly in open country, lying up by day in holes that he digs for himself or takes over from burrowers such as porcupines and aardvarks. Once, west of Olduvai, I found a "nursery" area with 17 mothers, numerous cubs, and a number of males. Dr. Kruuk has recently stated that spotted hyenas, at Ngorongoro, have a "clan" social structure dominated by females.

In marked contrast, the striped hyenas have never been observed in a pack, to my knowledge. The most I have ever seen together was a pair of adults with three half-grown cubs. These animals like bush country or thickly covered stream valleys that dissect the open plains. Much more truly nocturnal than the spotted hyenas, they are rarely seen. In the past their long shaggy coats and striped flanks earned them the name "tiger wolf," but they are certainly very unlike wolves.

All hyenas are linked with death in the minds of many Africans. Therefore it is—or was until recently—taboo to touch them. I remember from boyhood how distressed people would be if a hyena fouled the courtyard of a homestead. Members of that family were required to hold a purification ceremony immediately, to protect themselves from the risk of sudden death.

Everyone knew the danger present if a jackal—normally extremely wary of man—approached a human dwelling, and the Kikuyu gave such an animal a special name, *wamuthige*. Such "fearless" jackals were usually suffering from rabies. As a rule they made no attempt to attack dogs or men; the disease seemed merely to make them wholly unaware of any danger to themselves.

Solicitous caracal—the photographer's pet—curls protectively around her 4-hour-old kitten. A Swahili name for this strongest and most savage of the small cats, simba kali, *translates as "fierce lion." Black-tufted ears, green eyes, and soft unpatterned coat make it one of the world's most beautiful cats.*

ALAN ROOT

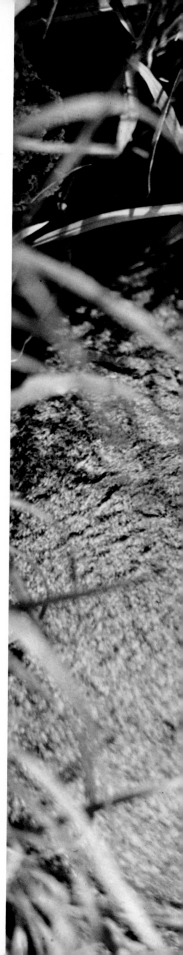

In the parks today jackals are growing more confident around humans. I have seen them come right up to sniff at the tires of a car, especially one from a household that keeps dogs. Of course, most zoologists — and I agree with them — assign both jackals and domestic dogs to the genus *Canis*, along with the wolf and the coyote.

Taxonomists currently recognize three species of jackals in East Africa, labeling them as the golden jackal *(C. aureus),* with a uniform reddish-yellow coat and dark tail tip; the jackal *(C. mesomelas)* variously called black-backed, silver-backed, or saddle-backed, with a dark tail tip and dark back patch sometimes touched with silvery gray; and the side-striped *(C. adustus),* with a pale slash from shoulder to hip and a white-tipped tail. This third animal, partial to wooded country and usually nocturnal, has not been studied to any great extent in the field, and I personally class it as a variant of the second species.

The commonest jackal, the black-backed, sometimes ranges in loose troops of as many as ten, keeping in view of each other within a few hundred yards, but they do not hunt as a pack as wild dogs or spotted hyenas will do. Apparently they move about in unison looking for the remains of a cheetah kill, or gazelle fawns that they can bring down easily. As soon as one finds food the others join in to gorge themselves.

All jackals will take small game, as well as rodents, lizards, birds' eggs, and some wild fruit. In farming areas the black-backed jackal is very fond of strawberries!

When I was young we thought of jackals as the local representatives of European foxes or American coyotes, and I remember the day my father came home from a trip out near the Ngong Hills and told us a remarkable thing — that he could scarcely believe his eyes, but he had seen "a real fox!" Then, of course, he checked with the newly formed Natural History Society in Nairobi and found out that he had seen *Otocyon* — commonly known as the bat-eared fox. As I grew older and went farther afield, I discovered that these little creatures were far from rare in open grasslands but very shy indeed and hard to approach.

T HE BAT-EARED FOX lives mostly on insects, including dung beetles and their grubs. Large herds of antelope and zebra graze on the open plains, where hundreds upon hundreds of beetles are busy all day long rolling up balls of dung from these herbivores. They bury the balls, each with an egg of their own deposited in it. When the larva hatches it feeds on dung until it becomes a pupa; during pupation it matures to the adult stage, ready to break out of the ball and fly away.

While bat-eared foxes do eat the adult beetles, they very much prefer the tender larvae. Evidently they can hear the scratching, squeaky sounds the insects make — noises I have detected lying down and listening intently. The fox walks along slowly over the plain, stops, digs down, and soon breaks open the ball and finds his prey. Since dung beetles nearly always bury a dozen or more balls fairly close together, the fox waits around and often locates additional morsels in quite a short time.

An even more remarkable feeding habit, which I have witnessed three times with bat-eared foxes, gave me my most exciting experience of watching wildlife when I first saw an example of it in 1932. We were excavating at Apis Rock, and on Sunday mornings I would stroll around

Leopardess and her young stretch sleepily on a low branch after consuming a Thomson's gazelle. Often considered Africa's cleverest hunter and most dangerous carnivore, the leopard usually stalks its prey alone, moving snakelike through the grass, then sprinting for the kill. At right, a mother and her cub exhibit the finely marked pelts coveted by poachers.

BARON HUGO VAN LAWICK (ABOVE); F. TURNER REUTER, M.D.

Snarling leopardess spats
with her mate in the
branches of an acacia tree
on the Serengeti. Seconds
later, both climbed down
and vanished in the grass.
A male cat will lay claim to
a wide area; if nothing
disturbs him and game
remains plentiful he may
stay for several years.
Proficient climbers, leopards
spend much time in trees.
Often they carry aloft game
they have killed, drape it
over a branch, and feed on
it for several days. They
prowl dense bush, thickets,
forests, or wooded river-
banks at night, and feed
or sleep through the day.

the base of the cliffs to watch the birds—a variety of starlings, several pairs of rather rare rock thrushes, many rock pigeons. I observed families of mountain kestrels and lanner falcons with special interest since I had never come across either before.

The lanner falcon flies along a cliff face, or darts among shrubs and bushes, until it flushes a bird into flight. It chases the fugitive like lightning and seizes its prey in midair. With a small bird like a rock thrush, the falcon carries its victim off to a rock ledge or a branch and eats it. A larger bird may give it trouble.

O N THIS PARTICULAR SUNDAY morning, I watched a pair of lanner falcons fly along the cliff face; I saw one scare up, chase, and seize a rock pigeon—so heavy that the falcon could not carry it off. The falcon extended its wings, using them as a parachute, and started to float down with the struggling pigeon in its talons. At that point I saw something I shall never forget.

Not far from me three bat-eared foxes were sitting outside their den. As soon as the falcon began floating down, they rushed to a point below it. As the falcon grounded, the foxes attacked it. They kept well away from its beak, but they pulled its wings and tail feathers. The falcon let go of its prey to defend itself and one of the foxes at once seized the pigeon and rushed away with it, disappearing down the den to be joined quickly by the other two.

At the time, I considered this incident unique and accidental. Since then, I have observed the same behavior on two other occasions. I now believe that the bat-eared foxes living near cliffs make a habit of watching for occurrences of this sort and thus obtain a meal they would never be able to catch for themselves. It must make a nice change of diet from dung beetles and their larvae.

If taken very young, bat-eared foxes can be tamed easily and make charming pets. They can be affectionate with their owners, but are most timid of strangers.

In the wild, bat-eared foxes show an extraordinary variability in numbers. Some years we see 10 or 15 families living within a few miles of our camp at Olduvai. Without warning they suddenly disappear, and thereafter it will be practically impossible to find even one family. Apparently this is due to a sudden swoop of disease—possibly distemper—that almost wipes out the stock. A few survive, and gradually build up a new population until the disease strikes once more.

Perhaps disease also curbs the numbers of the Cape hunting dog, but the loathing of stockmen may prove the greatest threat to this animal. The Kikuyu herdsmen at Kabete hated them because regularly, when they took their cattle and sheep west to an excellent grazing area called Ndeiya, they lived in constant fear that a pack of *mbawa* would come raiding. They told me that if the herdsman could intervene quickly

Sinewy forelegs and powerful hindquarters make the sway-backed cheetah an efficient runner (upper). The supple spine arches for longer strides, and the heavy tail helps this daylight hunter maintain balance on quick turns. A mother (lower) stands panting as her offspring begin feeding on the gazelle she has just killed. Litters normally number from two to five cubs.

enough, he could save his beasts—the Masai say this too. The dogs rush in so rapidly, however, and eat an animal so fast, starting to feed even before it is dead, that domestic herds frequently suffer.

Outside of national parks farmers and ranchers kill hunting dogs whenever possible, calling them vermin. Scientists working in park areas—for example, Wolfdietrich Kühme and George Schaller in the Serengeti—have given us a completely new view of these animals within the past five years. From the age of about three weeks puppies can digest meat, and they beg for it by thrusting their muzzles to the corners of the parents' mouths. Both males and females respond by regurgitating meat for them. Hungry adults that have stayed to guard the pups during a hunt are fed in the same way.

Once some companions and I found a secluded valley south of Olduvai where a number of dogs were looking after several litters. A few of the pups were nursing; others nipped playfully at each other. Their dark coats showed the reddish brown, black, and white blotching that marks the species. By the age of ten weeks the young would begin to follow the pack on the hunt. As we watched, the adults made no attempt to drive us away—a striking example of their usual lack of aggressiveness toward humans.

Normally one dog leads the hunt with others keeping back as much as half a mile, but as soon as the tiring gazelle or antelope turns sharply, zigzagging, another dog springs forward to maintain the pressure and eventually grabs its rump or flank and pulls it down. In this way a pack seldom takes more than a few moments to make its kill, once the chase has started in earnest.

I sometimes hear visitors express dismay when they first become really aware of how much killing is done by Africa's predators. At such times I am tempted to remind them that these animals kill almost exclusively for food, and that vastly greater numbers of game existed for thousands of years before being sharply reduced, and sometimes extinguished altogether, by that greatest of all predators—man.

Teardrop markings distinguish the cheetah, fastest of all land mammals. In hunting, cheetah rely on speed more than stealth, racing at 55 miles an hour. A chase of 200 or 300 yards exhausts them. At left, cubs wrestle after a full meal; within a year they will join in chases after game.

4

The Preyed Upon

Do the words "wild horses" make you think immediately of Africa? Probably not. Yet this is the one continent where numerous wild members of the horse family survive—the zebras. If you visit the parks of East Africa you will see them repeatedly, in lightly wooded areas or on the open plains, often in the company of antelopes.

While you certainly recognize a zebra, you may find the antelopes confusing at first, for Africa has a greater and more varied wealth of these than any other place in the world. In this chapter, I want to introduce this splendid array of species, for until you have met them you cannot truly realize the richness of Africa's fauna.

Watching any of these creatures holds a fascination of its own, for you can never quite forget that these are the preyed upon. If they fail in vigilance and speed they will die. Even the strongest and best-armed must be on guard. You may watch a herd of zebra moving in column toward a stream, and recognize that they are entering danger country —in the tall grass along its banks are lions. They move alertly; suddenly something gives the alarm, and they wheel sharply and gallop away.

Of the two species of zebra found in East Africa, the more easily observed is Burchell's, a stocky, short-eared animal with bold stripes especially broad on the haunches and rump. These creatures live in family units that gather in herds of varying size. In the dry season they migrate with wildebeest, traveling in search of good grazing and water.

At Olduvai, in 1931, my Kikuyu workmen found a partially eaten carcass of a Burchell's zebra that had been killed by a lion. They eagerly set to work to recover every tiniest scrap of the orange-yellow subcutaneous fat; they then rendered it into lard and bottled it. A few months later, when we went to examine fossil beds at Kendu Bay on Lake Victoria, I found them selling this fat to the local Luo people, charging ten shillings (about $1.75) for two or three ounces.

The Luo stated that they valued this fat highly as a general tonic. In earlier days the Kikuyu and the Masai had a more specific use for it— they considered it the only treatment for tuberculosis in its early stages. We still know too little about African beliefs of this kind, and I feel that the subcutaneous fat of the zebra deserves more scientific study.

Grévy's zebra is a taller animal than Burchell's, with large, heavily fringed ears and distinctive narrow stripes. It can be found from north of the Tana River into the Somali Republic and southern Ethiopia, in thorn scrub and arid plains. Kenya's two northernmost reserves—Marsabit National Reserve and Samburu Game Reserve—offer visitors a chance of seeing it.

The Grévy's range often overlaps that of the pale gray northern, or Beisa, oryx, while the smaller Burchell's zebra is occasionally found side by side with the fringe-eared oryx at Tsavo, the Masai Amboseli Game Reserve, and in parts of Tanzania. Both male and female oryx carry ringed horns, as long as three feet or more, almost straight and rapier sharp, and use them most effectively in self-defense. I have even seen records of their defending themselves successfully against lions.

Another large antelope which is ever willing to defend itself is the sable, now unfortunately a rather rare animal in East Africa. Trophy hunters for several generations have prized its long, robust horns, which curve sharply backward. Just recently Kenya gave complete

Throng of brindled wildebeest begins to wade the Seronera River in Tanzania on a seasonal migration to new pastures. Fear of predators in the tall grass alarmed the herd, and it trampled a yearling to death. One of the most widely preyed upon of East Africa's herbivores, wildebeest fall victim to leopards, hyenas, and Cape hunting dogs, as well as to lions.

protection to one small herd by establishing a new national reserve in the Shimba Hills, near Mombasa. These beautiful black antelope are still reasonably plentiful at a few places in Tanzania, particularly the Selous Game Reserve, some 200 miles southwest of Dar es Salaam. Their closely related cousins, the roan antelope, are rather more common, but both species are hard to see and still harder to photograph, being fond of open wooded country and shy by disposition.

The sable and the roan figure prominently in rock paintings in central Tanzania, where Stone Age artists recorded the distinctive white markings on the face, the roan's shorter horns and shaggier neck hair. In the earlier styles prehistoric men usually portrayed these creatures without showing the feet. This was highly naturalistic painting, since in fact one never sees the hoofs of such animals as they move through the grass of their habitat. Interestingly enough, artists of a later period painted the hoofs in great detail.

Africa's clowns, wildebeest cavort

Prehistoric artists also frequently painted the eland, easily recognized by its cattlelike build and dark-tufted dewlap below the neck. Almost certainly, Stone Age hunters took a special interest in this animal just as hunting tribes still do. It is the largest of the antelopes—a big bull stands almost 6 feet at the shoulder—and its meat is especially succulent.

ATTEMPTS have been made from time to time, and indeed still continue, to domesticate eland and treat them as meat animals. A government experimental station at Kabete kept a herd when I was a boy, and there I first saw an example of these creatures' astonishing ability to jump. Their paddock had a 7-foot wire fence around it, but one morning two bulls somehow got into a panic, cleared the fence with ease, and escaped. Since then I have witnessed similar feats on several occasions, and have never ceased to marvel at them, for eland certainly don't look like accomplished steeplechasers.

males often clash in ritualistic comb

In fact, when moving at speed they prefer to trot and just occasionally to canter; it is very difficult to get them to gallop. If pressed to a full gallop, they quickly tire. I regret to say that in the early days of farming in Kenya, when it was often necessary to shoot animals for food, farmers on horseback used to ride eland to a standstill and then urge the poor animals to a place near the farmhouse before killing them.

The elusive and rare antelope known as the bongo, happily, is now seldom hunted by trophy collectors, but both the male and the female carry spirally twisted horns and handsome striped coats that made them a very special prize a few decades ago. Sometimes they were brought to bay with a pack of dogs, a practice that has long been illegal. Bongo will stand to fight off dogs, and this made it possible for the hunter to approach close enough for a shot in the dense bush or forest they inhabit. Otherwise they were almost impossible to stalk, because they have an acute sense of hearing and very small delicate feet for so big an animal. They can hear a man approaching long before he has any idea of their presence, and instead of breaking into a run they slip away, silent and unseen. Today, at the Aberdare National Park, it is becoming increasingly possible to watch these beautiful creatures, especially in the very early morning at salt licks and water holes.

Antelopes as a group, including the gazelles, belong to the family

BARON HUGO VAN LAWICK

...e Masai Amboseli Game Reserve. Hoofs flying, a bull dances around another, leaping, bucking, spinning, and kicking;

assert dominance over their territories, resorting to such frenzied and antic displays when an interloper refuses to fight.

Bovidae, along with buffalo and domestic cattle. All have certain characteristics in common—for instance, all chew the cud—but they vary remarkably in many respects. At the other end of the scale from the large antelopes described above are many small but very different species, with the suni, or pygmy antelope—which stands about 12 inches at the shoulder—the smallest in East Africa.

Suni inhabit forest or woodland and are seldom seen in the wild except when they venture into glades or along open tracks. They do this at their peril since they are preyed upon by the larger eagles. If you examine the area around the nest of a pair of these birds, such as the martial eagle, you will often find bones and skulls of suni together with those of tree hyrax and small monkeys.

THE SUNI is often confused with quite a different creature, the dik-dik. These antelopes, of which there are some half-dozen species, typically prefer the drier bush country. They are slightly larger than the suni, and the short horns of the males are partially concealed by a tuft of hair. Their noses are long and very mobile.

Dik-dik are frequently seen but difficult to photograph, as they are exceedingly shy by day and dart into thick bushes when alarmed. In this way they escape from such enemies as jackals, caracals, and the larger eagles. The rather strong and unpalatable taste of their flesh tends to save them from hunters and poachers, but in some areas, especially along the Kenya-Somalia boundary, they are extensively hunted for the sake of their skins—it takes some 20, sewn together, to make a kaross for use as a floor mat or a bedcover.

After darkness falls, dik-dik seem much less afraid of humans, which suggests that they are more influenced by sight than by either sound or scent when it comes to detecting enemies. At night dik-dik will come right into one's camp and wander around, apparently without fear. In 1931 at Olduvai we found that sometimes we could walk right up to them with a flashlight and touch them.

It was also at Olduvai that I saw my first klipspringer. This stocky little antelope, some 20 inches tall at the shoulder, was named many years ago by Dutch settlers in South Africa because of its amazing ability to jump about on cliff faces. These creatures are very seldom encountered away from steep and rocky slopes; and they escape such predators as the leopard, cheetah, and serval by bounding up seemingly impossible cliffs. In other antelopes the hoof extends forward from the lowest joint, but the klipspringer's cylindrical hoof goes straight down to a surface which is flat like the toe of a ballet dancer's slipper.

I am always fascinated when I watch a klipspringer. As long as it stands motionless on a ledge, its coat blends so well with the background that it is practically invisible. Once it moves, it moves very fast indeed, bounding along where you would think no animal could possibly go. Then it stops again and seems to disappear. *Continued on page 92*

Migrating wildebeest stream across the Serengeti, over plains greened by recent rains; in May, as the dry season approaches, these herds head west to permanent water and grass near Lake Victoria, while others disperse into bush country in Kenya. In about eight months they will make the return trek.

NORMAN MYERS, BLACK STAR

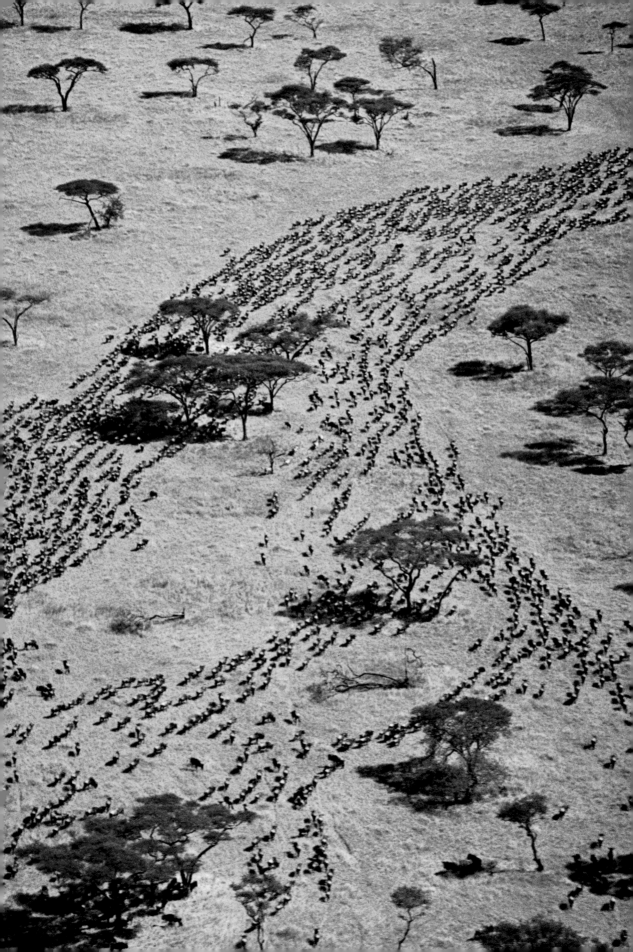

Ears forward and eyes alert, Grévy's zebra (above) pause warily in their grazing in wooded country northwest of Kenya's Samburu Game Reserve. While feeding they often scan the brush for lions. The taller of East Africa's zebras at almost 5 feet, Grévy's roam semidesert regions of Kenya and Ethiopia; at a distance, their close-set stripes blend into a landscape distorted by heat shimmer. In Ngorongoro Crater (left), Burchell's zebra —the more common species—struggle in a ritualized test of strength and dominance that lasted only five minutes and caused no injury. During the fight the stallions lunged with bared teeth at chest, shoulders, and hindquarters and kicked with their hind legs in an attempt to knock each other down. A young female will stay with her dam for about 15 months, until a stallion takes her for a mate; young males often remain with the dam as long as three years. Below, mutant patterning marks a Burchell's mare as a negative of her species' coloration. She—and her similarly marked foal—associate compatibly with a herd of normally striped zebras.

PAINTING BY JAY H. MATTERNES; GERTRUDE G. GAYLEY (BELOW); POPPERFOTO

Ringed by snapping basenji hounds wearing belled collars, a bongo in a mountain forest charges with lowered horns as a hunter reaches for his rifle. Elusive and rarely seen, the bongo will turn at bay and battle a pack of dogs, thus becoming an easy—and illegal—target. A greater kudu (lower left) guards two females that he herded into a thicket at the approach of a car. Greater kudu roam hilly bush country, feeding on leaves and wild fruit at dawn and dusk and resting during the day in secluded ravines. When attacked by a lion or man, the spiral-horned antelope gallops quickly away, but stops after a short distance to look back—a habit that sometimes proves fatal. Below, a troop of sable antelope stands in high grass. Formidable fighters, especially when wounded, sables kneel on their forelegs and sweep their scimitar-like horns in vicious, slashing thrusts.

In the race of klipspringer that inhabits southern Kenya and much of Tanzania, it is remarkable that both males and females have horns, for in other forms, whose range extends into southern and western Africa, only the males are horned.

THE DUIKERS are a widespread group of small to medium-size antelope that prefer forest or bush country. All have rather rounded backs, and males have short straight horns that slope in the plane of the forehead. Their plunging leaps of flight earned them their Dutch name of *duiker*, or diver. These animals range in appearance from the small and elusive blue duiker—actually gray, and hardly bigger than a suni—to the rare yellow-backed duiker, nearly 3 feet at the shoulder.

In East Africa the two common species are the gray bush duiker, with a dark stripe on its face, and the red forest species known as Harvey's duiker. The former is the one that Joshua hunted in my boyhood days. It will invade gardens in the suburbs of Nairobi and Nakuru at night to feed on unprotected rosebushes, particularly the flowers in bud. Harvey's duiker, also nocturnal, is exceedingly difficult to see and still harder to photograph, as it much prefers the dense thickets and forests to any other habitat. One variety, however, can be found in more open country along rivers and streams near the Kenya coast.

I first learned of the presence in Kenya of the largest of the duikers—the yellow-backed—in a rather surprising way. It had been recorded from forests in the Congo and Northern Rhodesia (now Zambia), but we had no really clear record from East Africa. Then one day after World War II, when I was curator of the Coryndon (now National) Museum, a member of the game department brought over a Dorobo hunter to see the exhibits. I showed this man around, and he was delighted to recognize many of the animals that we had on show and also to see others that he had never even heard of, such as the gorilla.

Suddenly he stood still and said, "There is an animal which comes from my part of the forest country which you have not got. Why not?" He proceeded to describe an animal that I had never heard of from East Africa, but I was able to make a guess at its identity from his account—a dark brown, almost black animal with a yellow dorsal stripe broadening into a wide patch over the rump. I told him I would like to see a specimen. When he returned to his home in the Mau Forest a few days later, he sent me part of a skin, a broken skull, and the horns of a yellow-backed duiker. Shortly after that we organized an expedition and established for certain the presence of a small population of this species in a limited area of our western highlands.

Equally rare and only slightly smaller is Abbot's duiker, uniformly blackish brown and so far only recorded for certain from the high forests and fringe of the moorland on Kilimanjaro and other slopes in Tanzania and Rwanda. Few people have had the chance to observe one alive, for it is very wary and mainly nocturnal. With such a restricted habitat both these species might seem to be in danger, but the cold, the dense forests, and also great stands of giant stinging nettles discourage hunters and poachers.

Swampy areas along slack-flowing rivers, marshes, and the backwaters of lakes comprise the habitat of the sitatunga, a handsome antelope

Licking her newborn calf, an eland gently cleans its coat. Minutes later it stood and began nursing. Largest of the African antelopes—bulls weigh as much as 2,000 pounds— the placid eland rarely charges hunters or predators even when wounded. It easily falls victim to rinderpest—a highly infectious diphtheretic disease that struck East Africa at the end of the 19th century.

Diverse array of horns distinguishes the heads of East Africa's herbivores; size, shape, and spread vary markedly not only among the different species but also among individuals within each species. Scientists theorize that the great variety developed through centuries of mutation, with the short spiky horns the most primitive. Though horns serve many purposes, the animals use them primarily in dueling. The bongo (22) uproots plants; the Robert's gazelle (9), by arching its neck, finds an efficient back scratcher. The animals here, all mature males (not painted to scale), carry horns typical of their kind. Identifications: (1) Topi; (2) Jackson's hartebeest; (3) Coke's hartebeest; (4) Hunter's antelope; (5) Brindled wildebeest; (6) Impala; (7) Gerenuk; (8) Grant's gazelle; (9) Robert's gazelle, a subspecies of the Grant's; (10) Thomson's gazelle; (11) Uganda kob; (12) Roan antelope; (13) Sable antelope; (14) Fringe-eared oryx; (15) Waterbuck; (16) Reedbuck; (17) Cape buffalo in four variations; (18) Lesser kudu; (19) Greater kudu; (20) Eland; (21) Bushbuck; (22) Bongo; (23) Sitatunga; (24) Oribi; (25) Dik-dik; (26) Suni; (27) Klipspringer; (28) Steinbok; (29) Gray duiker.

PAINTING BY JAY H. MATTERNES

almost 4 feet tall at the shoulder, weighing 200 pounds or more. Only males carry the long and twisted horns; but both sexes have splayed hoofs, four to six inches long, that enable them to move over marshy ground without sinking. These hoofs serve the antelope much as snow-shoes serve a man.

Sitatunga like to hide by day, either lying among the reeds or sub-merging themselves until only their faces remain above water. In my boyhood days it was practically impossible to see one alive. Today the Kenya Government is giving protection to sitatunga at a small swamp near Mount Elgon, while Uganda has established a sanctuary for them on an outlier of the Sese Islands in Lake Victoria. At both places it is now increasingly possible to get good daylight photographs.

Their cousin the bushbuck has a much wider range, but nevertheless keeps to forest, woodlands, and bush, always staying fairly close to water. A white band at the base of the throat, spots along the side, and stripes across the back account for one of the common names, "harnessed antelope." These markings are clearer on females than on males. Body color ranges from chestnut and dull red to nearly black in some males.

Locking horns, waterbuck battle in Ngorongoro Crater, possibly over the hornless female nearby but more probably over territory. The contest ended after several minutes of pushing, butting, and jabbing when one of the combatants fled into the trees; such fights sometimes end with the loss of a horn. At left, broken horn dangling, a bull pauses in a glade, his ability to defend himself seriously impaired. Waterbuck often plunge into deep pools to take refuge from lions, cheetahs, and wild dogs.

Deep in grass, a Beisa oryx (left) reveals the rapierlike horns and black and white facial markings that distinguish his species. The shy, fringe-eared oryx (above) derives its name from its narrow, black-tufted ears. Oryx, like some other African antelopes, can go weeks or even months without a drink, deriving moisture from plants.

Like the bush duiker, bushbuck are very fond of the young tender leaves of garden plants such as beans and sweet potato vines, and also the foliage and buds of roses, but their favorite feeding places are in forest glades or along the edge of streams. While the animal feeds it flicks its tail, and its ears are constantly moving backward and forward: listening, listening, listening for the smallest sign of danger. The moment it hears any suspicious noise, it freezes like a statue. After a time it may move one or both ears slightly, trying to pick up further sounds. You may notice this movement in cover, but often you first realize that a bushbuck has been quite close to you when it breaks into a frantic bounding leap for the tangled thickets.

For all its wariness and small size (only about 3 feet at the shoulder), the male bushbuck will readily attack almost any creature that seems to present a threat. I have seen a bushbuck seriously wound a dog, and once I saw one of these brave animals attack my old friend Joshua. We were out in a valley, checking his traps, and found a female caught by the leg. As Joshua approached, she bleated in pain. Suddenly, from nearby, her mate charged Joshua. The bushbuck struck with the forehead rather than the horns, but with sufficient force to send Joshua flying. When he picked himself up, I urged him to let the doe go free. He was more than glad to do so, and she bounded off to join her mate.

The reedbuck is nearly the same size as the bushbuck, but is easily recognized by its uniform rufous-to-fawn coat, its straight back, and the forward-curving horns of the male. Reedbuck does are hornless. These animals do not confine themselves to swampy areas as the name implies. At least one pair lives quite close to my suburban home in Langata. They normally prefer areas with grass long enough to afford plenty of

Overleaf: Rufous coats and blue-black haunch and shoulder patches characterize the topi. These hump-shouldered antelope, found in open country in Kenya, Tanzania, and Uganda, help maintain the quality of grassland by grazing on dry growth that inhibits seedlings from sprouting and easily catches fire.

cover. In early morning and again toward evening, they move about grazing. They will feed during the night, but throughout most of the day they lie up under bushes or in the shelter of tall grass.

Reedbuck are extraordinarily keen of hearing; they are usually aware of your presence long before you notice them, and until you come within a few feet they will not move. Then they make a bounding run for safety, uttering a characteristic whistling sound. All you see is a fast-disappearing animal with the white underside of its upturned tail flashing as it leaps through the high grass.

If you drive through the open, dry bush country near Longido in northern Tanzania, or on the thorn-scrub plain near Ol Tukai Lodge in the Amboseli Reserve, you can confidently hope to see one of the most remarkable of all the antelopes: the gerenuk. A single male, or a pair, or even a small group may stand warily among the thorns, staring at your car. You can quickly recognize the gerenuk by its long slender neck, lanky legs, and small wedge-shaped head, all of which inspired the common name "giraffe gazelle."

The male's ringed horns curve outward and then inward again; his delicate ears stand out as he listens. When he turns into profile you see that the horns swing gracefully back before the tips bend finally upward. The female is hornless, but in both sexes dark patches on the face seem to lengthen and enlarge the eyes.

Unless they have been badly frightened, the animals will start browsing again, moving slowly, with a strangely formal gait, to feed daintily on the leaves of more promising bushes. Suddenly one of the animals will reach up for higher branches; it will rise easily on its hind legs with assured poise, standing astonishingly straight. After balancing for a moment on its strong hind legs, it will extend a slender foreleg and rest it on a branch, bracing itself lightly. The reddish-buff of the back, the paler band on the side, and the almost-white belly help to emphasize this erect posture. In the shadows among the bushes the coloring stands out, while in sunlight the whole coat shines with a vivid gloss.

Undisturbed, the animals may drift from one bush to another, nibbling placidly. They can exist for days at a time without drinking, as their favorite browse contains a high percentage of water and their kidneys are adapted to make the most advantageous use of this supply.

If the gerenuk is one of the most specialized feeders among the antelopes, the impala is certainly the most graceful in movement and the most beautiful, as well as the most uxorious. I know no other species in which a dominant male controls so many females for himself.

Wherever you find impala—and they are widespread in East Africa, although always near water—you can observe two distinct types of association. In the first a dominant male controls a herd of hornless females and their younger offspring. The number varies; it is usually large, with 71 the highest figure I have counted. The second grouping, normally found not far from the first, consists entirely of males—the bachelor troop. Some are senior adults who have lost their harems to a challenger; some are almost in their prime, waiting their chance to challenge one of the dominant males. Others are yearlings, driven out of the harem by its master when they became too interested in the females.

Bachelor males frequently engage in play fighting, or sparring

Half-grown suni antelope will stand one foot high when mature. The photographer raised this suni from a one-pound baby, feeding it goat's milk and sweet potato leaves. It considered rose petals and green corn special delicacies.

Klipspringer pauses alertly before bounding to a rocky hillock nearby. These antelope —ranging in weight from 17 to 35 pounds—shelter on steep cliffs to avoid leopards, pythons, and servals, venturing down only to graze.

Red duiker, measuring 18 inches at the shoulder, crosses a clearing in the hunched gait characteristic of its kind. When alarmed, it darts into thick underbrush. Duiker normally live alone or in pairs, browsing mostly at night on leaves, berries, and bean pods.

matches, standing forehead to forehead, butting lightly and pushing gently with horns interlocked, and then jumping agilely away. When a bachelor challenges a harem-owner, a fierce battle will follow. The two interlock their horns, pushing and twisting. They often fight until exhaustion ends the contest; sometimes one of them may handicap his rival by breaking off a horn.

Impala both browse and graze. In either type of herd some individuals usually stand on the alert for danger, and any hint of it provokes prodigious leaps instantly taken up by the rest of the herd. Sometimes, when aware of a danger which they are unable to locate, they jump about in what looks like an indiscriminate manner—but always with immense grace—apparently trying to get high enough to see a possible enemy. As they dart about, they may fling themselves over bushes or over empty air or even each other's backs. Under these conditions a predator trying to concentrate on a single victim may lose his every chance in the confusion.

Many people consider impala venison excellent, but most of the hunting tribesmen I know avoid another fairly abundant antelope, the waterbuck, if they can find any game more suitable. This robust and handsome animal has a strong musky odor; I've tasted the meat and found it thoroughly unpleasant. Trophy hunters have killed the male for his long, symmetrical horns, but photographers greatly covet a good picture of the buck or a beautiful female silhouetted against the setting sun.

As their name implies, these antelope seldom stray far from water. They frequent reedy swamps, but also range through open bush country, so long as it is not too far from a stream or river. They prefer areas of long rather than short grass. Gregarious creatures, they not infrequently associate with impala or other antelopes.

Gregarious habits and a strong tendency to undertake local migrations are more noticeable in those species referred to collectively as plains game. These include the gazelles, the various hartebeests, the wildebeest, and zebra. Today the Serengeti Park in Tanzania, together with the Masai Mara Game Reserve across the Kenya border to the north, offers one of the few spacious strongholds for these animals. Here visitors can get an impression of their former abundance as it lasted for thousands of years until civilized man invaded their habitat and joined the ranks of the predators.

TOMMIES—as everybody calls Thomson's gazelle—are the most numerous animals of the plains communities. They are sometimes found in herds of hundreds and even thousands. Grant's gazelle, usually found in smaller numbers, share the open country with them. One characteristic gives the visitor a quick and reliable way of telling the two species apart. In Grant's a vivid white patch on the rump extends well above the root of the tail. The corresponding white patch on the Thomson's always ends below the base of the tail—which constantly wags with a jerky movement. The male Grant's, about 30 inches at the shoulder, is usually at least 6 inches taller than a Tommy buck and carries much longer horns. In both species the females have rather small horns; in Thomson's these are often misshapen and sometimes missing.

Not long ago I made a trip by air from Nairobi to Olduvai, and as we came in over the sunburnt plain, the pilot announced: "I'll just have to go down and buzz that Tommy off the landing strip. He's in quite the wrong place."

A single male was standing motionless between the whitewashed markers of our rather rough-and-ready runway near the camp. He held his ground until the plane roared low immediately above him. Then he dashed away, with the black stripe on his side flashing, but he did not go far. When we took off that afternoon he was still around, although there were no other gazelle in sight at any time that day.

In fact, that Tommy was in his rightful place. He was guarding his territory, which he had marked by rubbing a secretion from his pre-orbital glands (one on either side of his face) against grass stems and low bushes. As it dries, this secretion exudes a distinctive smell and warns any other male Tommy against intruding.

DOMINANT MALES are strongly territorial, defending their borders vigorously against any other males and even remaining to guard them when the females and young and the bachelors have moved away. Grant's gazelle have a rather similar system, differing in some details. Perhaps the feeding habits of the two species account for the differences to some extent. Thomson's feed predominately on grasses, while Grant's is basically a browser, preferring the leaves of small bushes and herbs. It can be independent of drinking water for long periods, meeting its liquid requirements like the gerenuk.

Gazelles have a peculiar gait called stotting, a kind of "bouncing along" with all four legs held stiff and straight, rather like the movement of a marionette. Fawns adopt this gait in play, and adults may use it when pursuing each other. At Ngorongoro Crater, John Goddard and Richard Estes—who was studying ungulate behavior with a research grant from the National Geographic Society—suggested that it may sometimes serve a warning function. They had seldom seen it in a context of danger until a pack of hunting dogs moved into the crater. Thereafter they noticed that gazelles began stotting whenever the dogs

Seeking refuge from scavengers, a leopardess drags a 50-pound Thomson's gazelle into a tree where she will feed on the carcass. Hundreds of thousands of Tommies throng the treeless plains of East Africa, providing an abundant supply of meat for many predators. Gazelles associate according to sex and age. Dominant bucks live alone on a home territory; other males roam in bachelor herds. Females with fawns band together, occasionally forming the harem of a solitary buck; they leave the herd to give birth in isolation. At left, half an hour after birth, a baby clambers to its feet.

BARON HUGO VAN LAWICK (BELOW); JOAN ROOT

appeared, and the display spread swiftly through the herd, with all the animals stotting before breaking into a gallop. This gait, also called pronking, occurs in other species as well, such as hartebeest.

Taxonomists group the hartebeests and their nearest kin in the tribe Alcelaphini. All the members of this group stand approximately 4 feet at the shoulder, which is distinctly higher than the rump, causing the back to slope. The common name kongoni, of Swahili origin, refers to Jackson's hartebeest, a reddish-brown animal found in Uganda and Kenya near Lake Victoria, and to Coke's hartebeest, a lighter-colored race found farther south. The horns of both Jackson's and Coke's rise from bony pedicels set high above the eyes; this upward prolongation of the face gives them a quite fantastic profile. A dark patch behind the shoulders, and a somewhat different shape of horn, distinguishes Lichtenstein's hartebeest, from southern Tanzania.

By far the rarest of this tribe is Hunter's antelope, a native of Kenya's northern semidesert regions. It usually has larger and more lyrate horns, a white chevron between the eyes, and a very wary disposition. I have never seen one of these alive, but we have found a number of fossils from an extinct variant at Olduvai Gorge.

THE TOPI, another member of this tribe, has a rich bay color with dark blue-black patches on shoulder and foreleg, hip and shin, especially in the males. As in other members of the group, one or two individuals normally take up sentry duty on the outskirts of the grazing herd. If possible, they stand on a vantage point such as a termite mound; if they snort in alarm, all gallop away.

Wildebeest—commonly known from crossword puzzles as gnu—are famous for the immense migrations they undertake. During the dry season they tend to associate in relatively small herds—from a dozen to a hundred or so—and wander about through bush country north and west of the Serengeti in search of water and grass that may be sprouting, fresh and green, after a local shower or thunderstorm. When the so-called short rains begin at the end of October or in November (sometimes even later), these small herds begin to congregate into larger ones. Then they start making their way toward the open plains, where grass has begun to sprout, and there the pregnant cows will drop their calves, mostly in January and February.

Thomson's gazelle fawn crouches on the Serengeti, concealed from a lioness by red oat grass and immobility. The Tommy froze when the lioness approached, while its mother retreated some 60 yards and stood stamping her forefeet and snorting in alarm. After the lioness moved past, the mother gazelle returned and the fawn sprang up and raced off with her.

Tens of thousands will sometimes move together, in single file or in serried ranks, grunting noisily as they march. It has been estimated that from December into May, some 350,000 wildebeest share the short-grass plains of the Serengeti with 180,000 Burchell's zebra and 500,000 gazelles. As the rains end, the wildebeest gather in great herds and the rut begins. When the vegetation begins to dry up, they move away, accompanied by the young calves, and scatter again into smaller groups, dispersing through the bush country in search of water and grass.

The sight of wildebeest on migration is unforgettable. Several times I have seen a column of these creatures moving out of the Ngorongoro Crater at Windy Gap, where age-old game trails are worn deep by the passage of many generations. I have stared, fascinated, as the herds came up the last lap of the fairly steep incline, moving at a fast walk; as they neared the top they broke into a run, crossed the narrow flat area

Sensing danger, impala vault toward sheltering forest in the Masai Mara Reserve, Kenya, covering 20 feet or more in a leap. A ram may control a harem of 70 or more females, dueling with other males to maintain dominance. After a vicious fight (left) a ram gores his adversary. Like most African antelopes, impala rarely battle to the death, preferring instead a test of strength that usually ends without serious injury; this ram seemed puzzled by his opponent's death. At right, a male bleats a warning at the approach of a possible challenger.

SARA CONN THOMPSON (ABOVE); THASE DANIEL

109

of the rim, and galloped down the other side to pause and reassemble at a small pan. There they drank and fed and rested before resuming the migration the next day.

Every now and then during the calving season I used to notice a few cows with two young calves and I assumed, not unnaturally, that these were twins. Now I know that generally the explanation is quite different. A few years ago at Olduvai we came across the body of a female wildebeest that was being devoured by hyenas and vultures. Her calf was standing helplessly not far away, unable to cope with the disaster, while a small herd of females with their own calves watched from a few hundred yards off. Suddenly one of these mothers, accompanied by her own infant, trotted over to the orphan, and it soon joined her. Since then we have witnessed this on several other occasions but, regrettably, it does not seem as though the orphans ever survive very long. Possibly these new "mothers" don't have enough milk for two, or perhaps they cannot keep watch over both calves and the orphan wanders off. It may die of thirst or, much more likely, be caught by a hyena.

When attacked by predators, wildebeest commonly rush away at a gallop; and yet sometimes they will unite to protect their young. In the Nairobi Park I once came across some 60 wildebeest cows forming a tight circle around their offspring and facing outward when a cheetah appeared to threaten the calves.

A NY VISITOR fortunate enough to see even a limited sample of our antelopes will go away cherishing some outstanding memory. It may be some dramatic episode of defense. It could easily be a peaceful glimpse of a superb animal, such as lesser kudu browsing at the edge of bush country at the foot of rocky hills in Tsavo Park in the early morning light. The hornless female is brownish-gray and blends with the dry grass, but the male is much darker. His white markings show more distinctly: thin white vertical stripes running down either side of the body, white at the base of the neck and throat and between the eyes. His spiralled, twisted horns may run to 30 inches or more, set on a finely molded head.

The lesser kudu's larger cousin, the greater kudu, stands 4 to 5 feet at the shoulder. It can still be found in East Africa, but unfortunately is becoming increasingly rare. In Tanzania the meat is relished by hunting tribes, and the huge horns are prized for making musical instruments—including the horns traditionally sounded in war. Another, quite different, use was made of one by Lord Baden-Powell, founder of the Boy Scouts. In 1907 he opened his first Scout camp, on Brownsea Island near Poole, England, with a blast on a kudu war horn he had captured during an uprising of Matabele tribesmen in southern Africa.

It would indeed be tragic if our modern protective measures failed to ensure the survival of the greater kudu. "Majestic" is the only word I know that adequately describes a fine male, and I shall never forget my first view of one—near Tendaguru Hill in 1924. He was standing in profile to me, ears spread, head raised, tensely alert, with eyes glittering as he tried to locate the source of a minor noise that I had inadvertently made—that had warned him of possible danger. He was the emblem of utter attentiveness, majesty and beauty.

Shy and elusive, a diminutive dik-dik crouches beneath the branches of a thorny acacia tree. This delicate 15-inch-high antelope—weighing less than ten pounds—falls prey to jackals and large eagles.

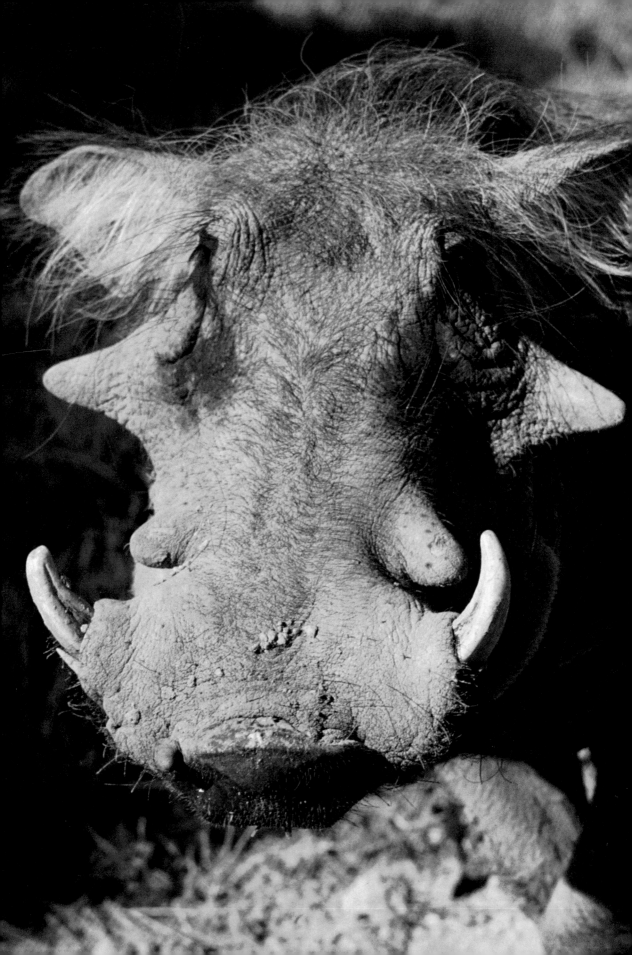

5

Aardvarks to Zorillas

For this assortment of animals I have selected some of the oddest and most entertaining creatures East Africa can offer. Few are truly rare, but many are so difficult to photograph under natural conditions that a good picture from the wild would count as a major trophy; reliable information about their habits is hard-won and valuable.

The aardvark, for example, seldom emerges from its burrow before eight or nine o'clock at night. In the open it looks very peculiar: the face elongated and narrow with a piglike snout, the ears large and donkeylike; the forelegs relatively short, the body massive, the hind legs muscular and powerful; the tail thick at the root and tapering about two feet to a point. Strong, straight claws arm the animal for digging.

Once when I was a boy my father decided to dig out an aardvark and get a really close look at it, but he and his men found it impossible. The farther they dug into the base of a hill, tracing its course, the deeper the aardvark went, and the earth it shoved back with its hind legs perpetually blocked the tunnel they were trying to follow.

Without undue effort the animal can dig into the base of a termite mound (the nest of the so-called white ant). Once the aardvark has broken through into the passages it starts to gather the insects with its sticky tongue, which it extends a foot or more.

Perhaps the most savage insects in Africa are the ants of the subfamily Dorylinae — sometimes called warrior or safari ants. A dense mass of them will kill any young animal trapped in a burrow, poultry shut into a yard for the night, almost anything that cannot get away. As a boy I tried to dig up a nest of these ants, but had to give up because of the pain of the bites. Yet twice I have found that an aardvark's last meal had consisted of tens of thousands of safari ants.

Our study of aardvark diet began when I was curator of the Coryndon Museum. A staff zoologist came to my office one day in 1945 and said, "Dr. Leakey, we've just opened an aardvark stomach, and do you know what is inside it?" I said, "White ants, I suppose?" "Yes, lots of white ants," he answered, "but also there are numbers of cucumber seeds!" This seemed extremely surprising, so I gave instructions for a letter to our local newspaper, asking anyone who came across a dead aardvark — killed by a car at night, for instance — to send it to the museum for a stomach-contents analysis.

The first seven specimens we studied included the seeds of a species of wild cucumber whose fruit grows underground. We set to work to find a reason for this. Some of our staff members located an area with several aardvark burrows and a single water hole. Each morning for a number of weeks they studied the night tracks leading to this water hole, and never once saw any trace of an aardvark going to water. Apparently the aardvark often meets his needs for liquid by eating wild cucumbers. Recently, however, we received an eighth specimen with no evidence of cucumbers at all. Maybe he was on his way to look for some when he was struck by a car.

The aardvark's common name of "ant bear" is misleading. This animal is so remote from any living relatives that it holds a unique status as the only surviving mammal assigned to an order all its own. Unlike the South American anteaters, which are toothless, the aardvark has five teeth, upper and lower, well back on either side of its jaws. They consist

Grotesque knobs protrude from the face of a 175-pound warthog boar. The warts reach greater size and prominence in the male than in the female. Upper tusks sometimes grow more than a foot long. Eyes high on his head enable him to watch for predators while he kneels on his forelegs to graze.

of tubelike structures of dentine, lacking enamel, and so gave rise to the name of Tubulidentata for the order.

On the whole, the aardvark's burrows and its tough skin seem to protect it from predators—and at least one old danger has been removed. Boer farmers, who named the creature *aard vark*, or earth pig, no longer hunt it for its hide, once used in making oxcart thongs and straps.

Dutch-speaking South African settlers also named the aardwolf, or earth wolf, another extraordinary animal that is rarely seen because it is nocturnal. It belongs to the order Carnivora, but its cheek teeth are quite unlike those of other carnivores—each consists of a single conical cusp—and it feeds primarily on insects.

I have occasionally seen aardwolves by car headlights, but only between nine or ten o'clock at night and three in the morning. Relatives of the hyenas, they resemble them a little in general build, with long forelegs and sloping back, but they are much smaller.

For a strange collection of features, few animals can compete with the elephant shrew, and I shall never forget the first day I saw one. This was in 1923, when I was in charge of supplies for a British Museum expedition hunting dinosaur remains in southern Tanganyika. One morning I saw a little creature about 10 inches long hopping about on its hind legs. I was very puzzled. I had never seen anything like it and had no idea what it was. I felt I must find out, and—I regret to say—I fired a shot and killed it, so that I could examine it closely. The long tail was rather like a house rat's, almost hairless. The body was covered with coarse black and red hair, and the nose was elongated like a miniature trunk. The teeth were clearly those of an insectivore.

I wrote to England asking for scientific literature on these animals (Macroscelididae to zoologists), and during the following eight months I saw many elephant shrews, both the black-and-red species, *Rhynchocyon petersi*, and a somewhat smaller brownish creature about the size of a squirrel, the soft-furred *Petrodromus tetradactylus*.

ALL OVER EAST AFRICA, from sea level up to 8,000 feet, you can drive along the roads with a good chance of seeing a small furry-tailed animal dashing along the roadside or crossing in front of you. This is the African ground squirrel, called *wakahare* in Kikuyu. We know little about this species in the scientific sense, but the little creatures figure again and again in East African folklore, where they take the place of Br'er Rabbit as examples of creatures of great cunning.

In fact, Br'er Rabbit and Br'er Fox—the folk-story characters made famous by Joel Chandler Harris—were derived from stories taken to America by Africans in the days of the slave trade. You may hear people speak of "rabbits" in Kenya today, but there are none native to Kenya. True rabbits give birth to numerous naked, blind young in nests below ground; baby hares are born in the open, usually one or at the most two at a time, with a full coat and functioning eyes, and are able to run within a few minutes.

Hares count upon escaping from their enemies—serval cats, jackals, and dogs—by sprinting over a short distance and then suddenly "jinking," turning sharply to the right or left and doubling back on their tracks so that the animal chasing them overruns them. As a boy, I found

Poking its scaly head into a termite mound, a giant pangolin (below) flashes out its sticky tongue to pick up the insects. In the drawing at right, an aardvark munches an underground cucumber, a source of water in dry thornbush country. Seeds found in the stomachs of dead aardvarks revealed their taste for the fruit. Also called ant bears, they feed primarily on termites and ants.

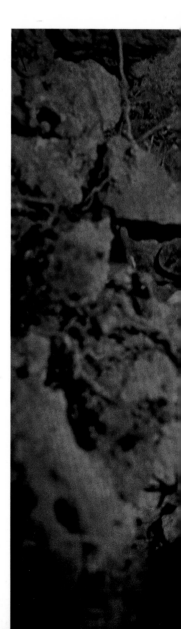

DRAWING BY JAY H. MATTERNES; POPPERFOTO

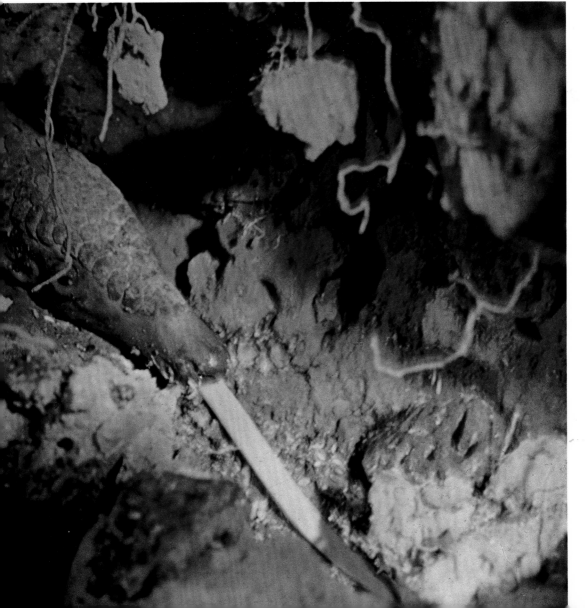

I could catch them after observing that a fleeing hare always carries its ears at an angle until just before it jinks, when it lays them flat on its neck. By always sidestepping to the right at the moment a hare put his ears down, I had a 50-50 chance that he would come straight into my hands and be caught! I can't help feeling that Stone Age man must have observed this same fact and turned it to his advantage.

In Biblical times men marveled at the ways of the animals around them. An ancient proverb, listing creatures "little upon the earth" but "exceeding wise," declared: "The conies are but a feeble folk, yet make they their houses in the rocks." This translation has caused some English-speaking readers to interpret conies as rabbits, but the Hebrew *shaphan* refers to the hyrax, a tailless creature scarcely the size of a big house cat and still found in Israel and the greater part of South Africa.

In East Africa we have examples of the three living genera of hyrax. *Procavia*, the rock hyrax, corresponds to the "coney" of the Bible. It lives in large colonies on rocky cliffs and disappears for safety into cracks and holes. It descends to the ground to feed on grasses and leaves. It sometimes shares its habitat with *Heterohyrax*, which looks very similar to the untrained eye, but differs in skull structure and many other characters. They never interbreed. *Heterohyrax* possesses wonderful balance and mainly feeds in trees and shrubs.

Dendrohyrax, the true tree hyrax, lives alone or in pairs, generally in forested country. Its fur, longer and silkier than that of the others, was once much sought after for rugs and ladies' coats.

Surprisingly the nearest known living relative of the little hyrax is the elephant; the creature's cheek teeth and skull, however, look somewhat like those of rhino in miniature.

I retain a vivid memory of an incident involving the tree hyrax, which is nocturnal and notorious for its incredibly loud and terrifying cries. During World War II there was a prisoner-of-war camp at Naivasha, some 45 miles from Nairobi, and one day an alarm went out that three Italian prisoners had escaped. I was one of those sent after them with some of my African staff because I knew the area rather well.

We headed for the Kinangop Forest, picked up their trail, and lost it again as darkness came. Early next morning a forest guard came to us and asked if I would come quickly to rescue three men who were lost and too terrified to move. Of course he had no idea who they were, but I guessed that these were our quarry and he guided us to them.

As soon as the escapees saw us, one of them called out in English, "Help, help, rescue us! We are so frightened—we were nearly killed last night!" "What by?" I inquired. "We do not know, we do not know, but the noise was terrible! Some animals were after us and every time we moved through the forest to get away another one was after us again." I asked what this noise was like, and they gave a loud, rasping, screeching sound—a fairly good imitation of the tree hyrax.

This was too good a chance to miss. I informed the prisoners that they were indeed lucky, since they had escaped the "notorious man-eating hyrax." We took them back to camp, and they quickly spread the tale of the dangers of the Kinangop Forest. For many months no one else tried to escape. Finally an Italian zoologist arrived in a new batch of prisoners, and he spoiled our story by *Continued on page 122*

Temminck's ground pangolin uncurls from a tight ball, its defensive position. Hard, sharp-edged scales overlap one another to protect the nocturnal creature. A prehensile tail distinguishes the tree pangolin (left); all species sometimes carry offspring on their backs or tails.

Continued on page 122

Emerging from their burrow, warthogs move out to graze on the semiarid plains of central Kenya. Common to much of Africa, they feed by day mainly on short grasses and keep to burrows at night. To avoid exposing their hindquarters to attack, they often enter the burrows tailfirst. When they run, the tufted tips of their erect tails bob jauntily with each short-legged step.

Ears cocked to a sudden sound, her two-week-old piglet at her side, a warthog stands poised to flee (opposite lower). These wild pigs emit muffled grunts as they feed, and some- times grunt loudly before fleeing in alarm.

Giant forest hogs nose up to a water hole near Treetops, a famous game-viewing hotel in Kenya's Aberdare National Park. Older boars, marked by semicircular shelflike growths beneath the eyes, weigh 400 pounds or more. Usually seen at Treetops in late afternoon or at twilight, the hogs move in sounders of from 4 to 20, keeping for the most part to heavily wooded areas.

T. H. CUNNINGHAM (TOP); SIMON TREVOR, BRUCE COLEMAN, LTD. (FAR LEFT); JEN AND DES BARTLETT, FROM "NATURE'S PARADISE," HOUGHTON MIFFLIN CO.

119

*Searching for insects, a forest elephant shrew hops along a wood-
land floor in Kenya. This creature's common name offers no clue
to its scientific classification within the order of insectivores. Actually* Petrodromus tetradactylus *bears only a distant kinship
to the shrews and owes the "elephant" to its long mobile snout.*

*Not a true hare despite its name, the spring hare can bound as
far as 15 feet. Its head and body length: 15 to 25 inches. This
rodent frequents grasslands of eastern and central Africa.*

*Bristling with armament, an Old World
porcupine waddles toward its burrow. The
rodent charges with a backward rush when*

GEORGE B. SCHALLER, NEW YORK ZOOLOGICAL SOCIETY

attacked, jamming its sharp, detachable quills into its adversary; the tips often work deeper into the flesh, causing festering sores. Rarely seen during the day,

porcupines forage largely on roots and bulbs. Adults grow to weigh 40 pounds or more. Africans prize the animal's tender flesh and use its quills for ornaments.

121

explaining to the others what these fearsome night noises really were.

Most of the East African mongooses are nocturnal, the chief exceptions being the banded and the so-called pygmy mongoose. Both of these often go around in small troops rather than alone or in pairs.

The pygmy mongoose is common in the coastal belts, but extends far inland and even to the Olduvai region. It occurs as a pet in many households. Given an egg, an animal of either species will stand with its back to a wall or a pole or a tree, holding the egg in its forepaws, and then throw the egg between its hind legs to break the shell — a technique used in the wild to break open the eggs of guinea fowl or other birds.

Banded mongooses, as well as pygmy mongooses, often occupy disused termite hills, coming out during the day to forage — mainly for insects and nearly always as a unit. The most I have seen together was 30, in a troop near the Namanga River at the Kenya-Tanzania border.

Of the nocturnal mongooses, the white-tailed is the most common, frequently seen in car headlights. It patrols the roads by night to feed on small creatures killed by traffic.

P ANGOLINS, nocturnal mammals that look somewhat like prehistoric reptiles in their armor of overlapping scales, still suffer to some degree because of sheer superstition. Many African tribes have considered the scales of the giant species (actually modified hairs) as magic. One morning in 1932, when I was camped with members of my third archeological expedition on the eastern shore of Lake Victoria, several fishermen speared one of the large Temminck's pangolin, a burrow-dwelling species, in the edge of a swamp, and began plucking its scales.

"What do you want those for?" I asked. "They're magic," came the reply. "Magic in what way? Why all of them?" "Because, Bwana, we can sell each of them for five shillings." This was about 85 cents a scale — and each pangolin has hundreds and hundreds of scales!

I persuaded the fishermen to give me the carcass for its skeleton, and when we opened the stomach we found a few remains of termites (recorded as the pangolin's principal food) and, to our surprise, the remains of hundreds of water beetles. Then we realized why so often we encountered pangolins by the edge of the lake at night.

As we found later by watching on moonlit nights, the pangolin goes down to a swampy backwater and lies partly submerged with its mouth at water level. It moves its long tongue about on the surface. Water beetles immediately start swimming around to investigate, and then adhere to the pangolin's sticky tongue.

Scale-collecting so far as I know has never endangered the two species of smaller tree-dwelling pangolins, which spend much time hidden among the branches. They should be safe as long as our forests remain.

In our animal alphabet, P stands for pigs, including the warthog, *Phacochoerus aethiopicus*. It is at once the most common and the most comical of the African wild pigs. Its diurnal habits and grassland habitat make it the most easily observed as well. Visitors can readily watch it feeding, kneeling on its forelegs, snout close to the ground, back sloping, rump high; or running off in alarm, with legs twinkling busily and the tail carried straight upward, the tufted tip wobbling floppily about.

BARON HUGO VAN LAWICK (ABOVE); GEORGE B. SCHALLER, NEW YORK ZOOLOGICAL SOCIETY (BELOW LEFT); ALAN ROOT

Pygmy mongooses peer from their shelter in an abandoned termite mound on the Serengeti. Young animals, like the month-old banded mongoose at left, tame easily and make affectionate pets. A black-tipped mongoose (right) feasts on plover eggs.

When I was writing a report on East African fossil pigs in 1958, I undertook a study of the living warthog. Among other things I analyzed stomach contents of a number of specimens at the Museum. The results surprised me. I had expected roots and leaves and a variety of vegetable foods, but I found little other than small grass blades. As I dissected the facial warts that inspired the common name, I found them full of thorn-tips in the dry seasons but almost free of such things during the rains. Then, watching warthogs graze in very dry weather, I found that they had to search for food at the base of small thorny plants, nudging them aside. As they did this, many thorns broke off in their warts and the process scratched their upper tusks. On the basis of my observations I concluded that these upper tusks are not used as defense weapons but as special tools when feeding.

It is the short lower tusks which serve as weapons; but I have observed that the warthog relies mainly on flight to save itself from leopards, lions, or other predators.

One day in 1929, when I was excavating at Gamble's Cave near Lake Nakuru, I went out on the plains and deliberately chased some wart-hogs. I wanted to witness the behavior I had so often heard about—that when pursued a warthog often will gallop to a burrow and go down it backward, keeping his face to the enemy.

The warthog I followed did exactly as I had been told he would. He dashed to his burrow, stopped abruptly, whirled through 180 degrees, and started down the hole in reverse. As I got close the animal came charging out again with a terrified squeal. Behind him emerged a spot-ted hyena! On seeing me the hyena also fled, while I could do nothing but laugh. Obviously the hyena, after taking over the warthog's home, had treated him as the intruder.

Unlike the warthog, the bush pig, as his name implies, likes dense cover. He has a wide range but, being nocturnal, is hard to see. Unless you have a dog with you, or a keen nose for scent, you can easily go past a clump of bushes where these pigs are lying up for the day, but if you do locate them you may disturb a group, or sounder, of 10 or 15 individuals. If they rush off through the undergrowth you may notice that they carry their tails hanging down, not upright as warthogs do.

In recent years the number of bush pigs has increased alarmingly where leopards have been killed off, and they do great damage to crops.

The rarest of our wild pigs is the giant forest hog, named for its bulk and specialized habitat. In all my years in Kenya I have only once seen a wild one. A boar ventured to cross a cultivated area between two patches of forest near Kabete. Women working in the fields gave the alarm, and very soon men and dogs were chasing the pig across country. Eventually the poor creature was killed when it was too tired to run any farther. Nowadays, a campaign has developed to eliminate both the rare giant forest hog and the bush pig from areas adjoining farmland to protect domestic swine from disease as well as to reduce crop damage by the bush pig. At places like Treetops, however, visitors have a good chance of seeing a group of the impressive forest hogs at the salt licks or water holes.

Nothing seems to check our population of porcupines. I can still hear my sister Julia saying plaintively, "Father, the porcupines have been at

Venturing into forest, a zorilla warily eyes a 5-foot gaboon viper, a deadly

snake that preys on small mammals. A days-old aardwolf (below right) keeps close to its mother in a cave near Mount Kenya. At left, below, a badgerlike ratel feeds on bony scraps. Ratels often follow honey guide birds to wild bees' nests. The ratels raid the nests for honey; the birds eat the wax of the combs.

it again." She had just come up from our vegetable garden by the stream, where these large rodents once more had dug under the fence and destroyed a large share of our carrots, turnips, and potatoes.

Very widespread, porcupines live in burrows, which they dig for themselves, and emerge at night to find food. Although they eat many kinds of wild fruits and roots, they much prefer garden crops.

A great enemy of the porcupine is the marauding safari ant. Man, too, kills porcupines whenever he gets a chance. They continue to flourish, however, and I see no real risk of their being wiped out.

AFRICAN BEEKEEPERS lose a great deal of honey and many a hive to the ratel, or honey badger, but if they are wise they are very cautious about interfering if they catch one feeding. About the size of the related European and American badgers (although somewhat differently marked with a black coat on the lower part of the body and a pale gray cape running from forehead to tail), the ratel has earned its reputation of being a terrible fighter. With a determined bite and long strong claws it can inflict severe wounds, and it has a tough hide for defense. It regularly kills small mammals or reptiles to supplement a diet that otherwise includes honey, wild fruits, roots, and berries.

A favorite entertainment at Olduvai, when we have visitors, is to take them out to see a colony of spring hares in the glare of car headlights. These rodents, with a body length of about 16 inches and a very long furry tail, move by hopping on their hind legs like miniature kangaroos. If you're agile enough you can grasp a hare by the tail before it vanishes down its burrow. Spring hares make remarkably good pets; several of our friends in Nairobi keep them in their gardens.

At the end of our alphabet stands the zorilla, a handsome little animal with a black body marked by broad white stripes. One seldom sees it by daylight. In Africa you often hear it referred to as a "skunk," because like the true skunk it defends itself by emitting an oily spray with a highly offensive odor. Understandably enough, photographers have had little success with this creature in the wild, and very little is known of its behavior. I feel it is well worth studying. Who would not admire the staunch observer who set out to record its ways, hunting it along the roadsides, keeping watch for it in the late hours of the night?

Nocturnal tree hyrax feeds on tender leaves in a Maytenus tree. To the uninitiated, its spine-tingling call—a crescendo of throaty croaks punctuated by a high-pitched scream—conjures visions of some man-eating beast. At left, a pair of Heterohyrax *laze in the sun in Serengeti National Park. The hyrax's tusklike upper incisors and the arrangement of its limb bones link it to the elephant, its nearest living relative; however, the two share no common ancestor later than the Eocene Epoch, 45 million years ago.*

F. TURNER REUTER, M.D. (ABOVE); R. I. M. CAMPBELL

6

The Primates

Our closest cousins among the primates are the exuberant chimpanzee and the sedate gorilla. It was the existence of these two species and the fact that both inhabited the continent of Africa that led Charles Darwin, a century ago, to write: "It is...probable that Africa was formerly inhabited by extinct apes closely allied to the gorilla and chimpanzee; and as these two species are now man's nearest allies, it is somewhat more probable that our early progenitors lived on the African continent than elsewhere."

I believe that Darwin's words approached the prophetic, for I have long been convinced that Africa is the birthplace of man and that his presence there can be traced back millions of years.

The word "primate"—which groups men, apes, monkeys, and prosimians, and sometimes includes our incredibly distant relatives the tree shrews of Asia—signifies "the first" or "the leader." We and our cousins differ greatly in appearance and intelligence, of course, but we are linked by certain unmistakable characteristics.

With a single exception—the tree shrew, considered an insectivore by some authorities—primates have fingers capable of picking up and holding objects in a firm grasp. Flattened nails instead of claws distinguish the fingers and toes of most of them—and most have five fingers on each hand and five toes on each foot. The eyes of the higher primates (men, apes, and monkeys) are placed close together on the front of the face so they can look directly forward at the same time, their fields of vision overlapping almost completely to provide depth perception.

The most important characteristic shared by primates is a brain that is large relative to body size and weight. This feature becomes more and more strongly developed the higher we go on the evolutionary scale of the primates. Man stands unchallenged at the top, his brain so complex that even now it is taking him toward the stars.

Of the many different primates that evolved in past ages, a proportion failed to adapt adequately to their surroundings and so became extinct. Those that survive—in East Africa and elsewhere—have adapted to existing environments. Man, of course, has frequently modified his environment to suit his own purposes and desires.

Although many forms did become extinct, a great range of living primates can still be found. Far down the evolutionary scale we find East Africa's little prosimians, the nocturnal bushbabies and the pottos, with some characteristics like those of earlier ancestral creatures that never evolved as far even as the monkeys. They keep the naked, moist skin around the nostrils that you see in your cat or dog, and they still depend heavily upon their sense of smell. Scent as well as touch and hearing remain important to them as creatures of the night. The huge eyes of these prosimians indicate that vision serves them well in darkness. If you find one curled up in a hollow tree by day, it often seems too sleepy and dazzled by light to escape.

Furry and winsome as kittens, bushbabies reputedly acquired their common name from their chattering high-pitched calls, like a wailing human infant's. Scientists recognize the cat-size species as *Galago crassicaudatus*, or thick-tailed galago, and a smaller type as *G. senegalensis*. In dry thornbush country I have seen the latter hunting insects before the light failed completely; the larger bushbaby is often found in gardens

Shy and reserved, the mountain gorilla long had a reputation for ferocity that field studies now have dispelled. Threatened by extinction, the peaceable apes retreat steadily up forested mountains of Uganda, Rwanda, and the Congo as man and his cattle take over the lower slopes. Mature males, called silverbacks for the saddles of grizzled gray hair they develop, head bands of some 5 to 20 subordinate males, females, and young.

129

in the suburbs of Nairobi and will come down from the trees before darkness falls, if tempted with such bait as a banana.

On the ground, bushbabies may move on all fours; alarmed, they leap away on long, powerful hind limbs. In the trees they display their true skills, clinging upright to a branch, then springing astonishing distances to another. Bushbabies have survived with little change since the Miocene Epoch, clinging and leaping among shadowy branches—behavior that many primates must have shared some 40 million years ago.

Recently scientists have found ways to observe and photograph nocturnal animals without disturbing them, by using infrared scopes and lights. In 1968 the National Geographic Society granted funds to a team led by Dr. Gerald Anthony Doyle of South Africa to study bushbabies by these methods, both in the wild and in seminatural laboratory conditions. Soon we may know to what extent galagos exert dominance within a group, how one group reacts when it meets another, and how mothers rear their young.

Pottos offer marked contrasts to the galagos. Small, rounded ears crown a domed head; woolly brown or gray-brown fur adds bulk to a foot-long body; short muscular limbs match a very short tail. While the bushbaby springs gracefully about, the potto clambers up a tree, hand over hand, with slow, deliberate movements, or climbs down headfirst. Hard pressed, it can move 10 feet in less than 3 seconds.

The potto, which gives off a sharp musky odor, has developed some odd specializations. The index finger has shrunk to a stump, leaving a hand adapted for clutching branches in a powerful grip. A unique structure marks the back of the neck—blunt spines covered by skin project slightly from several vertebrae. The reason for this is not understood, but I have observed that when the animal shows aggression, the fur that normally hides these spines tends to open away from them.

Long reported as rather solitary and normally shy, the potto keeps to forests around Lake Victoria in Uganda and Kenya, and along the Kenya coast. Its range extends westward to the Atlantic.

Neither of these prosimians makes a good house pet. The potto is far too apt to bite, and its teeth can strike to the bone. Bushbabies look terribly attractive, but when taken as pets they are almost impossible to house-train; they spray urine on their hands and feet, presumably to identify their territory in everything they touch. The faces of both hardly change expression, in contrast to the rich array of grimaces, scowls, and frowns of the higher primates.

MONKEYS show primate evolution well on its way. Keen vision has become all-important by day in judging treetop distances. East Africa's monkeys include the most beautiful of all, the members of the colobus group. Primatologists find them especially interesting because of the specialized structure of their large stomachs, which enables them to digest a steady diet of leaves.

In the past, Africans and Europeans alike hunted and trapped them for the sake of their long, silky pelts, to make tribal regalia or trim for ladies' wraps and hats or "throws" to drape over furniture. Most attractive of these monkeys are the members of the black-and-white species, *Colobus polykomos,* with varying white markings on the shoulders and

Clutching a grasshopper or gripping a branch, these little primates share one thing—the hand—that sets their order apart from all other creatures. Below, harsh daylight shrinks the pupils of a wide-eyed, nocturnal galago. The galago and its slow, deliberate cousin, the potto (right), belong to the primitive suborder of primates called prosimians.

ALAN ROOT (BELOW); JEN AND DES BARTLETT, BRUCE COLEMAN, LTD.

flank and a long white or white-tipped tail setting off the glossy black.

Colobus monkeys exhibit strong evidence of territorial behavior. A single troop of these animals will occupy a well-defined range in the forest; an experienced observer can usually find such a troop within an hour or so, but good photographs of colobus in the wild are very rare indeed. The black-and-white animals don't stand out in forest shadows, and when they bask in the sun they are usually in the high branches, hidden by layers of leaves.

Laws protect the colobus in Kenya, but the game department may make exceptions. While seedlings of a reforestation area are growing, the forest workers are allowed to plant potatoes, corn, peas, and other vegetables. Inevitably, forest animals enter these plots—bush pigs, giant forest hogs, and monkeys, including the colobus. Probably it seeks nothing but leaves of certain weeds and, possibly, sweet potato vines (which it will accept as food in captivity). The farmer nevertheless tends to blame any animal he sees for damage to his crops, so he requests that a game scout be sent to shoot the raiders. I would like to see an investigation of the stomach contents of every colobus shot in these circumstances, to determine where the blame belongs. Some dealers take advantage of the law. A man selling colobus skins sometimes tries to claim, falsely, that he acquired them legally.

Another species, the red colobus *(C. badius)* carries a glossy black cape that extends from the forehead along the back to the thighs; the rest of its coat gleams chestnut red. It keeps to the warm lowland forests of Kenya, Tanzania, and Uganda, with a range extending to West Africa. Although the red colobus in the wild seems unwary, little is known of its behavior, but a study is now being carried out in Tanzania. One variety (possibly a race rather than a full species) is found only on Zanzibar Island. This is Kirk's red colobus—a spectacular monkey marked in chestnut, black, and white.

All the red colobus seem unusually delicate, unable to adapt to changes of temperature, climate, and food. Captives pick at food, and usually die within weeks or months. Any attempts to move wild groups from one habitat to another would require intense and prolonged studies of the new area and of handling techniques. At present, unfortunately, the small population of Kirk's colobus is in real danger. Tanzanian law gives it some protection, but it risks being killed off nevertheless. Farmers make no distinction between it and the vervet monkey, a bold and diligent raider of crops.

Triangular black faces distinguish the little vervets, generally the most common monkeys of East Africa. Scientists put them in the genus *Cercopithecus,* or guenons, but disagree over the number and characteristics of species and races. Vervet coats vary with age, individual, and locality—from brownish-olive to grayish in color.

Many of the troops near farms and villages show little wariness of man. In Tsavo National Park vervets come right up to join a picnic and grab food from lunch baskets. Exasperated farmers trap them all over the countryside, for vervets flourish practically anywhere, from the coastal plain among the palm trees right through to the driest bush, wherever they find leaves and fruit for food and trees for refuge.

In spite of their wide range and abundance, I believe vervets are an endangered species, chiefly because they have been greatly in demand for medical research and in the production of vaccines.

Almost anywhere in East Africa's higher-altitude forests, you can find either the Sykes' or the closely related blue monkey, larger than the vervets and fairly thickset, with cheeks rounded over the mouth pouches into which they stuff wads of leaf to chew later. A typical Sykes' from east of the Great Rift Valley has a white band around the neck with a white gorget in front, white tufts on its ears, and red-brown coat with black arms, feet, and tail-tip. Blue monkeys found west of the Rift are black and gray, with thick, long coats of beautiful soft fur for which hunters used to kill them.

In some southern areas in Tanzania, however, the Rift Valley ceases to separate these groups; and there you see intermediate forms. Therefore some scientists, like myself, regard the Sykes' and the blue as extreme subspecific variants of a single species, *Cercopithecus mitis*. Others class them as two full species.

Sykes' monkeys make amusing pets. Mary and I have had them on several occasions, but we have found that to keep them in the house is sometimes very trying. They break things out of sheer exuberance. Many NATIONAL GEOGRAPHIC readers will remember our Sykes' monkey Simon. One day when we were out of the house he got into our drinks cabinet and pulled out every bottle of liquor. When we came back, we found an appalling mess of bottles and broken glass on the floor, and in the middle lay poor Simon, very much "under the influence." He recovered, in due course, but after that we were more careful.

Over many years, I have tried to trace the behavior patterns of Sykes' monkeys in the Karura Forest Reserve near Nairobi. I used to go there frequently, and I could be absolutely certain of finding a troop somewhere within its home range. The monkeys would remain in view high up in the trees, and I have watched them feeding and grooming

Rarely photographed, Kirk's red colobus exists in the wild only on Zanzibar Island. Extinction threatens the monkeys as landowners shoot them to protect crops. Unable to adapt to changes in temperature, climate, and diet, the delicate species resists translocation. Below, primatologist Cynthia Booth, working at the Tigoni Primate Research Centre near Nairobi, records data on colobus skulls. She has stuffed the skins with cotton and wood shavings.

Grooming a female with young, a vervet monkey rids her of
dirt and parasites. A common social contact among primates,
grooming maintains friendly relations within a troop. Above,
a female stands to peer over vegetation. She has ventured to
the ground to search for insects, spiders, and grubs — and
possibly to raid a farmer's crop. The blue scrotal skin of a
dominant male (below) fades when age and challengers force
him to take a subordinate rank. Laboratories the world over
have used vervets in cancer and organ-transplant studies
and in the search for a German measles vaccine. Trappers
catch thousands of vervets a year in East Africa for export.

Diverse guenon genus includes numerous species and sub-species, their coloration and fur patterns varying enormous-ly. Black faces identify the scrappy vervets, and a nose like a blob of putty character-izes Schmidt's white-nosed monkey. The goateed De Brazza's grips a fig stem firmly between palm and fingers. A white neck band distinguishes the Sykes' from its close rela-tive, the blue. His forest hab-itat destroyed by cultivation, the blue holds a sweet potato taken from a farm.

PAINTING BY JAY H. MATTERNES

Vervet monkey with offspring

De Brazza's monkey

Schmidt's white-nosed monkey

Sykes' monkey

Blue monkey

138

themselves. I have never seen them engaging in such intimate behavior as mating, however—probably because they were fully aware of my presence and very carefully watching me in return.

Both Sykes' and blue monkeys seem in some danger, and their handsome relatives, De Brazza's monkeys, are threatened with extinction in East Africa. Most strikingly marked of the guenons, these have unmistakable white goatees and a band of chestnut hair on their foreheads. They prefer to live in gallery forests along streams and rivers, and more and more of these trees are being felled with the expanding development of agriculture as new areas are being taken over for settlement. I believe that it will be essential to move De Brazza's monkeys from their shrinking natural habitats into a national park or other protected area.

It should be possible to establish new breeding groups of these monkeys, for they have already been bred successfully in captivity. At the Tigoni Primate Research Centre, near Nairobi, primatologist Cynthia Booth bred De Brazza's monkeys regularly over several years, although she found them difficult captives. They fought each other so fiercely that it was a problem finding any two that could live together. A magnificent big male that once tried to attack her later spent a good deal of time beating up two mates.

While working with the De Brazza's she made a fascinating discovery: These animals have three different and distinct coats during their lifetimes—a "natal coat" when newborn, then a juvenile coat, and finally the coat of an adult. Other African monkeys have only two distinct coats; their juvenile and adult coats are virtually indistinguishable, but the natal coat is softer in texture and different in color. When an infant reaches the age of about six to eight weeks, coarser hair begins to replace the natal coat, which in most cases is entirely lost by the second or third month. As long as the natal coat remains, it produces a strong protective response from adults of both sexes.

Of all the African monkeys the patas is the only one that has specialized in speed on the ground. Slender and long-legged, it compares to the stockier baboon as the cheetah compares to the leopard. The patas walks, canters, or gallops quadrupedally, dashing over the grass with a gait like a greyhound's and a speed recorded at 35 miles an hour. It sometimes stands fully erect for a short time to look over the tall grass of the savanna. It ranges the width of the continent, enjoying savanna country between the equatorial forests and the Sahara.

Since patas groups prefer open arid country, and may range as far as seven miles in one day, they pose problems for the observer. Nevertheless, the late Professor K. R. L. Hall carried out a field study in Murchison Falls National Park in 1963.

Even at a distance, Hall could distinguish between various adults. Crown, nape, and back vary from brick-red to brown in both sexes, and the female has the same white "mustache" as her mate, but she averages

Simon, a pet Sykes' monkey, lies across the shoulders of Mary Leakey, the author's wife. The De Brazza's (lower) wears three distinct coats during its life. At birth it has a soft natal coat that evokes a protective response from adults. After six to eight weeks the coarse brown juvenile fur begins to appear. As the monkey matures it turns gray.

Overleaf: Mountain gorillas, shaggy coats protecting them from the cold of the heights, cluster in undergrowth where they feed on giant celery, thistles, and other vegetation. Awkward in trees because of their great bulk and weight, mature gorillas remain on the ground most of the time. As night approaches they bend and break foliage around them to make nests for sleeping.

only half his size and weight. His total length may reach 60 inches, half of it tail. Pure white fur gleams on his underbody, rump, and hind legs; females and juveniles wear a modest fawn color.

One adult male, 4 to 12 females, infants, and juveniles formed the social unit observed by Hall. This harem pattern is shared only by the hamadryas baboon and the closely related gelada among nonhuman primates. The male stands sentinel, going several hundred yards from the rest to survey new terrain from a tree or from high ground, watching for a leopard, a man, a baboon troop, or other patas. If he spots a lone adult male near his family, he breaks his habitual silence in an agitated burst of contralto barks. Patas keep a wary eye on big game, and calmly keep their distance; they withdraw rapidly if baboons approach.

Like baboons and other monkeys, patas pluck food with their hands —leaves and seeds, fruits and berries, insects and mushrooms—from the ground or from trees. Unlike other monkeys generally, their group scatters at night; mothers guard small infants, but otherwise the patas disperse to separate trees for shelter.

Specialists disagree on how to classify the patas. Some place it among the guenons; most assign it to a genus of its own, *Erythrocebus*, because of its specialized anatomy and behavior.

OMPARABLE RIDDLES plague the taxonomist who considers the genus *Cercocebus*, the mangabeys, and the extent of its kinship with baboons, those specialists in success on the ground. The gray-cheeked and the black mangabeys stay high in the canopy of low-altitude swampy forests; other species rarely venture above lower branches, and spend much of their time on the forest floor. The common term "white-eyelid monkey" singles out a conspicuous mark of this genus: Strikingly pale lids and adjacent skin, bright on a dark face, distinguish four of the five species. Presumably the eyelids play an important expressive role in signals within the group, as among baboons, which flash lowered eyelids as part of a threat display.

Mangabeys share another characteristic with baboons and their forest-dwelling kin of West Africa, the drills and the mandrills: The females have an area of bare red skin around the genital region, which swells conspicuously when they are in season. And although we know little of mangabey behavior in the wild, their vocalizations show certain resemblances to those of baboons. Several studies are now under way.

Personally I prefer to classify the mangabeys with the baboons, as members of closely related genera.

To me, baboons are the most interesting of the monkeys, and second only to the great apes for interest within the whole primate order. Their range extends throughout sub-Saharan Africa, except for parts of the western coast above the Gulf of Guinea and a large region stretching south through the Congo basin. They thrive in the open plains, but some troops extend their activities into the woodlands.

Sturdy and powerful, baboon males may weigh more than 100 pounds. Heavy muscles ripple under the thick ruff of hair on their shoulders. Strong jaws mark their doglike muzzles; their razor-sharp canine teeth are often as long as a lion's. Females lack these formidable weapons, and generally reach only half the weight of the male.

BARON HUGO VAN LAWICK

142

Playful, mischievous, and inventive, chimpanzees tussle in Tanzania's Gombe National Park. Considered the most intelligent of the primates after man, chimps modify natural objects for use as tools. At left, one of the apes picks termites off a stem that he stripped of leaves and thrust into a passage in a termite mound to fish for the insects. The animals also fashion crude sponges of lightly chewed leaves for sopping up drinking water from hollows in trees. Baroness Jane van Lawick-Goodall, working with National Geographic Society support, first reported chimp toolmaking.

143

Troops commonly range in size from 40 to 80 individuals, including members of both sexes at all age levels. In each big troop a male or a small group of males dominates the rest. These are animals in their prime. Both males and females show complex ranks of dominance and submissiveness, with flare-ups of aggression.

Because baboons often roam accessible country and quickly get used to human observers, we now have excellent field studies by Hall, Sherwood Washburn of the University of California, Irven DeVore of Harvard, and others. Such reports may give interesting clues to what man's ancestors must have done when they left the refuge of forests and invaded the grasslands.

Other observers are now studying baboons in a more forested habitat where, apparently, the animals can survive with a much looser social organization than open country permits.

My own first real contact with baboons came when I was not quite 20, on the British Museum expedition looking for dinosaur fossils in southern Tanganyika. I had seen baboons in very small numbers from my boyhood days, but they were not at all common around my home. Down at Tendaguru Hill, in a forest habitat, I found several large troops of the yellow baboons, *Papio cynocephalus*. On two occasions, moreover, a baby baboon was brought to me after a leopard had killed its mother, and in each case I tamed it and kept it in my camp.

Later I met baboons in large numbers elsewhere and at Olduvai Gorge, where there are several troops. We know one of these better than the others because its range covers the eight-mile stretch where we have carried on our main excavation work since 1931. I remember a day when Mary and I were working at site SHK. The baboons were resting at the top of the cliff some 200 feet above us, where a number of small trees grew right at the brink. One young male, more inquisitive than the others, moved out to the extreme end of a branch overhanging space. Quite suddenly the branch broke under his weight and the poor creature crashed about 40 feet onto the scree slope below. He lay there screaming in pain, and we felt sure he had broken an arm at least. We moved up as quickly as we could to help him.

Tension yawn of a male baboon reveals formidable canine teeth. Lowered white eyelids signal his displeasure. Afraid to attack the objects of his anxiety—two baboons fighting—he sits and threatens impotently.

Until that moment the rest of the troop had remained where they were, chattering and very nervous. As soon as they saw Mary and me coming up from below, however, five of the biggest males came scrambling down over that sheer face. They reached the wounded baboon well ahead of us, and promptly helped him up the cliff and away. I've never seen a more efficient rescue; it clearly reflected the cohesiveness of the baboon social unit.

As man has killed off the leopard for his pelt, the baboon population has risen sharply. Their troops not only raid crops, but also deplete the supply of wild fruits and plants. I would like to see the balance restored by letting the number of leopards increase.

Baboons sometimes share the same forest area with chimpanzees,

Bib of pale fur earns the white-collared mangabey its name. Some taxonomists tentatively class this monkey and the baboons as close relatives, evidenced by their similar white eyelids, "barking" calls, reproductive organs, and facial expressions. Largely tree-dwellers, mangabeys feed on seeds, leaves, and fruit.

145

Occasional killers, baboons supplement their diet of fruit, grass, roots, and insects with small animals when the opportunity for an easy kill arises. Below, a mature male feeds on a small antelope. At left, a female with a nursing infant grooms an adult male. Dominant males customarily receive more grooming than they give, picking at a female for a few seconds, then being groomed in turn for 10 to 15 minutes. At right, a curious young baboon chews on the rear-view mirror of the photographer's Land-Rover.

and Jane Goodall and her husband Baron Hugo van Lawick have studied the interactions of these two species in what is now the Gombe National Park in Tanzania. They have watched baboon and chimpanzee mothers sit calmly while their offspring play together almost as though they belonged to one species. Yet, on occasion, a group of chimps will kill and eat a young baboon.

At times individuals of the two species will fight over some delicacy such as meat or fruit. The monkeys will bark loudly and slash with their long canine teeth, while the apes scream and strike downward with their powerful arms.

One simple distinction among the members of these two animal families is that apes, like man, have no tail. Another important difference appears in the torso. Monkeys have deep but narrow bodies, and their internal organs are arranged much like those of other quadrupedal mammals. Apes, like man, have broad chests, and their viscera follow the pattern best adapted for a nearly upright posture — signs of their close relationship to human beings. Even more significant is the fact that apes greatly outrank monkeys in intelligence.

Chimpanzees are not known in the wild anywhere in Kenya, but fortunately they are common in forests of western Uganda and still thrive in two areas on the eastern shore of Lake Tanganyika, in Tanzania. In a forest south of the town of Kigoma, a team from the Japan Monkey Centre is studying the apes. The other region, of course, is the Gombe Park, the area made famous by Baroness Jane van Lawick-Goodall in her book *My Friends the Wild Chimpanzees*, published in 1967 by the National Geographic Society. In months of patient note-taking Jane learned to recognize individuals and patterns of chimp society. Among her many findings was the fact that a mother and her offspring form the only stable group.

Chimps band together for hours or days, wander off on their own, or leave one assemblage for another, roaming at will. The normally vegetarian chimps will kill and eat monkeys, and they even make crude tools — chewing and crumpling leaves to sop up water, stripping twigs and grass stems to fish termites out of their mounds.

Jane has by no means completed her work. She is still engaged in following up the lives of the chimpanzees and hopes to determine how long chimpanzee family ties persist and to trace the relationship of one youngster to another from infancy to the adult state.

Chimpanzees share with the gorilla the distinction of being man's closest living relatives. Serological tests of their blood yield reactions much like ours. They resemble us in many other ways, including the psychological. Thus, unfortunately, the medical profession finds them valuable for research — in compatibility studies for tissue transplants, for instance. I only hope that this demand for wild apes can be reduced. These creatures may not survive at the present rate of capture and export from Africa. If we need them for research (and frankly I would rather not see them used), then we should breed them in captivity and not take wild ones from their wonderful free lives in the open.

Too expensive and too powerful to be commonly used as a research subject, the gorilla is largest of the living primates. Rising on bowed hind limbs to slap his massive chest, a mature male of the mountain variety stands 4½ to 6 feet tall. He has a saddle of light-gray hair in his glossy black fur; this patch gives the fully mature male the name of silverback and distinguishes him from the younger males and the females. His muscular arms span 8 feet easily, but his weight of 300 or 400 pounds, nearly twice that of a female, makes him move with more care in the trees—and climb less frequently—than youngsters of his own kind or chimps of any age. Both apes, however, make nests of leafy branches or grasses and sleep in them stretched out or curled human-fashion, in sharp contrast to monkeys, which sleep comfortably sitting up.

As farmers and pastoralists invade the forests, the mountain gorilla faces grave danger of extinction. I would like to see an agency such as the International Union for the Conservation of Nature and Natural Resources given authority to maintain a sanctuary providing absolute and permanent security for these animals, whose range overlaps the borders of the Democratic Republic of the Congo, Rwanda, and Uganda.

A NOTHER FORM of this great ape, the lowland gorilla of West Africa, also seems endangered. Logging roads cut through the coastal jungle, and the gorillas retreat to steep hills unsuited to cultivation and into insect-ridden swamps. With funds from the National Geographic Society, Dr. Clyde Jones of Tulane University in New Orleans, Louisiana, has studied lowland gorillas in Río Muni.

Miss Dian Fossey from California is now making a study of the mountain gorilla, whose behavior varies from animal to animal and from group to group. This follows earlier studies of mountain gorillas by Dr. George Schaller. Sponsored by the National Geographic Society, Miss Fossey has already completed a year's observation in Rwanda. Within four months, she had learned enough of the gorillas' gestures and sounds to trade signals with them; they no longer fled in alarm, but accepted her presence. For example, by crossing her arms over her chest, hands on shoulders, she can convey submissiveness.

All gorillas beat their chests, in various situations or moods; and she learned to imitate significant differences of rhythm, phrasing, and volume, by the rapidity and intensity of strike. She has concluded that the silverback which dominates his group often will chest-beat to signal the location of his band and question the location of another. If another group is within earshot, its dominant silverback will respond.

Time and again she has jotted down examples of the gorillas' reticent study of her. Once, during the creatures' midday siesta, two silverbacks sat side by side, both fully intent: "For some reason they reminded me of bejeweled ladies sitting in front-row seats at the opera—subtly trying to peek over their shoulders and take in all they can, and at the same time trying not to give the impression they're staring."

On one occasion Dian caught a group's reaction to a new noise, the wail of jet planes overhead: "They tried to locate it with much head-turning, but their eyes kept level with the hills in back of them."

Such field studies are now giving us important new knowledge of these great primates, which can survive only if man leaves them free from perils they cannot avoid or comprehend. Let us hope that before it is too late we humans can manage to live peacefully among ourselves as successfully as the gorillas have done.

Propped in a woody shrub, a juvenile patas monkey peers at an insect caught for food. Unlike most monkeys, long-legged patas can move faster on the ground than in trees; observers have clocked them at 35 miles an hour. One adult male and several females and their young form the normal social unit. The male remains apart, watching for predators. Noisy diversionary displays distract enemies and warn the other monkeys, who scatter into trees or hide in tall grass.

THASE DANIEL

7

The
Vanished

Africa today has such an amazing variety of wild animals that sometimes we tend to forget that our Stone Age ancestors and cousins lived in the midst of a great wealth of animals of very many kinds, some that have continued to this day and many more that are now extinct. I myself certainly did not begin to appreciate this fact until my first season at Olduvai Gorge in 1931, when we began to find the fossilized remains of strange animals side by side with stone tools.

One morning my student Donald MacInnes and I were exploring site HWK in the side gorge, where erosion gullies flank the red-banded outcrop called the Castle. We came across three enormous molar teeth, each a handful in itself, and quickly called Dr. A. T. Hopwood, the paleontologist of the expedition.

After looking at them with unbelieving eyes, he said: "Louis, this is completely and utterly impossible! In the past few days we have established that Bed I contains humanly made stone tools—and now the presence of these teeth of *Deinotherium* shows we must be wrong. It just cannot be true. We have made a terrible mistake somewhere."

"But Hopwood," I replied, "it is not a mistake. We can easily prove that these teeth came from the same deposit as the stone tools. What must be wrong is the existing theory."

It certainly looked as though the evidence had got mixed up somehow. *Deinotherium* belongs to the order Proboscidea, which includes elephants living and extinct; its teeth are unmistakable; and so far as anyone knew, it had become extinct long before man came into existence. We wondered whether these teeth were, perhaps, what are sometimes called "derived fossils." If so, they belonged to an earlier deposit elsewhere which had been broken up, and its contents had washed into the deposit with the stone implements. That at least was a possible answer. But it was not long before we knew for certain that there was no such mix-up. Additional finds showed quite clearly that at Olduvai Gorge *Deinotherium* and tool-making man had been contemporaries.

This settled, our next question was: Just what was the significance of these facts? Were the Olduvai deposits very much older, geologically, than we thought? These teeth certainly suggested as much. Alternatively, had this huge animal survived much longer in Africa than elsewhere?

We know today that the answer lies in a mixture of these two ideas. In 1931 we believed that Bed I, the deepest and therefore earliest stratum at Olduvai, was 500,000 years old. Now we know, from potassium-argon dating and other new methods, that its early deposits date from nearly two million years ago. Moreover, it seems that a great number of animals persisted in Africa somewhat longer than on other continents before dying out completely. The fact that *Deinotherium* reportedly disappeared from Europe about four million years ago does not make Bed I that old. Even at that time Africa was a land of surviving giants.

From the beginning of our work, *Deinotherium* forced us to reconsider problems of time concerning early man and the animals he knew. In 1960 an enormous specimen of this creature, with tusks five feet long around the curve, gave us a clue to man's range of skills, for we found stone chopping tools scattered among the bones of the skeleton. Apparently the beast had died in a swamp and a foraging party had cut meat from the carcass. Presumably they ate their feast raw, however, for we

African tigers of a million years ago feed on an eland much like the living species. While no fossil evidence can exist for the cats' striped coats, a jawbone found in 1957 indicates that tigers, extinct in Africa today, once lived at Olduvai Gorge.

PAINTINGS IN THIS CHAPTER BY JAY H. MATTERNES, BASED ON STUDIES OF VARYING AMOUNTS OF FOSSIL EVIDENCE, SIMILAR LIVING SPECIES, AND CONSULTATION WITH THE AUTHOR AND OTHER AUTHORITIES.

Giraffes of the past and of the present gather beneath an acacia tree taken, like all vegetation in this series of paintings, from current landscapes. Wide palmate horns crown Libytherium, *a creature that lived through nearly all the two million years of the Pleistocene Epoch, disappearing in fairly recent geologic times. Present-day giraffes indicate the size of the vanished species. The smaller okapi, another giraffid, evidently roamed the savannas with* Libytherium; *it survives today only in dense rain forests of the Congo.*

153

have never found a sign of fire in any of the main fossil beds of the gorge.

Deinotherium was not the only archaic proboscidean reported from Olduvai deposits. For years it had been thought that a mastodon had been present also. Broken chunks of two rather flattened tusks, examined in cross-section, exhibited a dentine structure characteristic of some mastodon species. Imagine, therefore, our surprise when one day in 1942 my wife Mary found the jaw of a gigantic extinct pig and then one of its upper tusks. This tusk, despite the fact that it certainly belonged to a pig, was over three feet in length and exhibited all the characteristics of the supposed Olduvai mastodon! We know now that the animal which carried it reached the size of a present-day rhinoceros, yet we have found its bones in the litter of ancient campsites or living floors in the upper levels of Bed II.

Since fossil pigs have always been one of my special interests, I named this wondrous new pig after Mary, and she has never been quite sure whether she should consider it as a great compliment, or not, to have the world's largest pig named after her! Actually it was a very great tribute to her and her work. Nicol being her maiden name, I designated it "Nicol's African pig"—*Afrochoerus nicoli.*

This magnificent species, kin to the modern warthog, is by no means the only enormous pig hunted by our early Stone Age ancestors and cousins. A similar giant was related to the bush pigs of today, and a third related more distantly to the giant forest hogs. There were also some eight other extinct pigs which have left no living descendants.

Some of these extinct pigs are fairly closely related to those of Asia. This resemblance between East African and Asian fossils is particularly interesting. It recurs as a theme again and again, in spite of the fact that today the two continents hold very different living faunas. Asia has no giraffes or hippos, Africa no bears, no tigers, no deer. Evidently in the past the land bridges between these continents were wider, and no deserts like those of the Sahara and Arabia kept animal populations apart. Africa and Asia had more animals in common, and allied species showed closer resemblances than they do today.

OUR FIRST SEASON at Olduvai brought a dramatic bit of evidence to light. Hopwood rushed back to camp one day and announced to the rest of us: "I have found teeth of what looks like that strange extinct short-legged giraffe—*Sivatherium*. I cannot imagine what it is doing in the middle of Africa, but I am sure that that is what it is!"

For almost a century this animal had been known to science, but mainly from one area: the famous Siwalik Hills deposits in the southernmost range of the Himalayas. Like *Deinotherium*, the sivathere was supposed to have become extinct well before man appeared in the world. Yet here was *Sivatherium* in Africa, and high up in the sequence, in the upper part of Bed II with well-made hand axes. This great find, made at the very beginning of our first season's work, altered our ideas of animal distribution in place as well as time. Numerous subsequent discoveries have confirmed it and, incidentally, shown that the valid name of the African genus is *Libytherium*, "the beast from Libya."

One tantalizing puzzle remains unsolved—this massive giraffid carried large palmate appendages, a little like the antlers of a moose, and nobody yet knows precisely how and at what angle these structures were held on its head. We can reconstruct it with good probability since we now have the greater part of a skull cap with broken "antlers," but no complete skull has yet been found. That is one of the fascinating things about studying the past; you know a certain amount, and you always know there is additional information just around the corner.

Another remarkable cousin of the giraffe is the okapi. From Bed I we have remains of several *Okapia* fossils. Today it is a rare animal found exclusively in parts of the dense rain forests of the Congo. Yet its nearest relatives were widespread in eastern Europe and Asia more than ten million years ago, and we can regard the okapi as a real example of a living fossil.

About one million years ago, when Olduvai was a land of giants, an immense oxlike creature flourished among them, boasting enormous horns. The horn cores alone span more than six feet; the keratin sheaths that covered them may have increased this by half. These horn cores provided a major find for the first scientific expedition to explore the gorge, a German party led by Professor Hans Reck in 1913, when Tanganyika was a colony in the German empire. He obtained a weathered specimen, the back part of the skull with horn cores in place; and, finding sheeplike characters in the cores, he named the creature *Pelorovis*, "monstrous" or "prodigious sheep."

Since 1952 we have found a complete skull, several complete limb bones, and many other specimens of *Pelorovis* at site BK II in the side gorge, and in 1967 my colleague Dr. Alan Gentry published a study demonstrating that this animal in fact belongs to the tribe Bovini, with the buffalo as a surviving relative. We discovered its shattered leg bones among stone tools and waste flakes near the top of Bed II, with more nearly complete remains in a clay-filled gully. Possibly the tool-makers drove their prey into the mire of this gully, killed it while it floundered there, and dragged it out again, sometimes leaving an unusually large or deeply bogged victim behind. It seems probable that because of its immense horns *Pelorovis* could not flee as speedily as more agile animals and so fell easier prey.

The fleet-footed creatures certainly included horses, for two types continue from Bed I through Bed IV: a conservative, comparatively primitive three-toed species, and the modern, one-toed *Equus oldowayensis*, a prehistoric zebra. Antelopes of varied sizes occurred at various times as well, ranging from large to small, and the preyed upon included hares and small insectivores and rodents.

A jackal indistinguishable from the living black-backed species spanned the whole Olduvai sequence and appears at many other sites, but a much rarer fossil from Bed I and lower Bed II is of special interest to me. It represents an extinct species of the dog family, *Canis africanus*, rather larger than a jackal. I have sometimes wondered whether it does not represent the true ancestor of the domestic dog.

Among the extinct members of the cat family in our Olduvai deposits, we have discovered another ancient link with Asia. In Africa today, of course, the lion is the dominant large cat, while its counterpart in Asia, from India through Southeast Asia and north to Siberia, is the tiger. A few wild lions still survive in India, and *Continued on page 162*

Sweeping horns identify **Pelorovis,** *bovids related to the present-day Cape buffalo included here to show the immense bulk of the extinct species. Stone Age hunters may have trapped and killed these creatures by*

driving them into the mire of a gully until they became helplessly bogged. Yellow-billed oxpeckers
and cattle egrets, birds borrowed from comparable scenes today, feed on parasites and other insects.

Treasure-house of prehistory, Olduvai Gorge slices deep into the Serengeti—and two million years into the past. Here

At Olduvai Dr. Leakey examines a fossil **Deino-therium,** *an extinct giant related to the elephants. Son Jonathan rests on a water tin. At right, Dr. Leakey stands beneath a horn core of* **Pelorovis.** *The skull of a present-day ram, one horn stripped to the core, suggests the span of the huge bovid's horns in life.*

the author and his team have unearthed a remarkable array of fossils, including giant species long since vanished.

*Nomadic Masai tribesmen wait at Dr.
Leakey's free clinic at Olduvai Gorge
for treatment of their ailments. At
right, curious baboons investigate
the author's Land-Rover as he tours
Nairobi National Park with Dr. Leonard Carmichael, Chairman of the
National Geographic Society's Committee for Research and Exploration.
Society grants help Dr. Leakey carry
on his work at Olduvai.*

RAPHIC STAFF

Links to a vanished past: Part of a million-year-old elephant tooth (on hat) and a broken Deinotherium *molar attest to the author's careful excavations. Born in Kenya, he early acquired the patience and keen eye that have rewarded him with scores of significant discoveries.*

161

they were certainly present in the Near East in Biblical times—the captain of King David's guard "slew a lion in the midst of a pit in time of snow." On the other hand, Africa now has no tigers.

The overlap of lions and tigers, however, appears to have been widespread at one time. In 1957 we found the largest fossil jaw of a felid yet recorded from the gorge, and its shape is more like the present-day tiger's than the lion's.

When I was a student at Cambridge, the laboratory assistants used to say: "If you get the jaw of a big catlike animal to identify in practical tests, sir, do not worry looking at its teeth. Just put the jaw on the table and try to rock it. If it rocks it be lion, if it don't it be tiger." This simple

method of identification still stands. The jaw of a tiger rests with a three-point contact on a table, while the jaw of a lion has the lower margin curved like the rockers of a rocking chair so that if you put it on a flat surface you can tilt it back and forth easily. Our fossil mandible from upper Bed II stays as steady as a tiger's on our laboratory table. This does not mean, however, that the big cat of Olduvai was striped like a modern tiger. It may have been, but naturally we cannot be sure.

I suppose the strangest animal that we find as a fossil at Olduvai is the creature known as a chalicothere, famous in zoology as proof that life is stranger than theory. Baron Cuvier, the founder of modern paleontology, concluded that if you find certain kinds of teeth, suited to a diet of plants, you will *always* find that the animals which owned them had hoofs. Not long after he died in 1832, chalicothere remains established beyond question that certain animals with the teeth of herbivores had flourished in the past—with great claws on their feet! Some of the most primitive chalicotheres had five toes; later types reduced this to four claws, or to three. Features of the skeleton place all these creatures in the order Perissodactyla, with horses, tapirs, and rhinos; the claws indicate some highly specialized habit, but no one knows what it was.

A possibility that interests me greatly is whether some surviving form of chalicothere might be the origin of the strange stories that we hear throughout East Africa, of what is commonly called the "Nandi bear." Several tribes, especially those living in forested regions, have stories of a very rare animal the size of a donkey, with a sloping back high at the shoulder and low at the rump, like a hyena's. Tradition has it that this is a very fierce creature and that although it lives mainly on vegetation it also eats flesh, tearing animals apart with its claws. While I would certainly hesitate to make any prophecy that a chalicothere still survives in Africa, or that the tales of the Nandi bear are based upon it, I feel that the possibility cannot be excluded completely. That living fossil the okapi remained unknown to science until 1900, when the explorer Sir Harry Johnston sent specimens to London. After all, if an okapi has survived why should not a chalicothere have done so?

No account of the fossil animals of Olduvai can be complete, because we are finding new creatures all the time. Already our reports describe more than 160 species that lived side by side with early man and his cousins. The main gorge alone contains some 150 miles of fossil-bearing exposures, and we have worked about 5. We know almost 50 sites we would especially like to excavate, and we have dug fewer than 15. Other sites in East Africa also promise great rewards, and some of these take us much farther into the past.

At Fort Ternan, east of Lake Victoria, we possess an unusually rich site some 14 million years old. Here we once found 1,200 fossils in just two months, including a little giraffid about the size of a calf, a medium-size mastodon, a small rhinoceros. Here, most important of all, we gained an invaluable clue to the background of man. My senior African assistant, Heslon Mukiri (who retired in 1968 after working with me for four decades), discovered and excavated a fragment of upper jaw that suggests developments in our own ancestry. For example, the canine tooth is considerably smaller in size than we find in living and extinct apes. Other characters foreshadowing human development appear in

Giant extinct pigs—Afrochoerus nicoli—*dwarf modern relatives, knobby-faced warthogs.* Afrochoerus *once ranged from the Transvaal to Algeria, foraging near water. Here the long-tusked giants wade among Nile cabbage.*

Crashing through papyrus clumps, massive deinotheres
—"huge beasts"—send hippos splashing to safety in
deeper water. These big proboscideans may have provided
food for early man, who could cut flesh from the carcass
of an animal trapped in mire. Tusks measured as much
as 5 feet. Protruding eye sockets of the extinct Hippopotamus gorgops *distinguish them from today's spe-*
cies, H. amphibius. *Chalicotheres at right—claw-*
footed creatures related to horses, tapirs, and rhinos—
range an ancient savanna. Claws may have served the
chalicothere well for defense and for digging up tubers,
but they undoubtedly made him a slow, clumsy runner.

closely related specimens from the Siwalik Hills: evidence that increases the interest of this species which I named *Kenyapithecus wickeri.*

Now, at early Miocene sites—Songhor, and Rusinga Island in Lake Victoria—we have found remains of a new species which I have named *Kenyapithecus africanus.* Fossil primates of such great age are rare, and when comparative material is scanty, scientific assessments are always subject to change. In my opinion, however, these new fossils—teeth, jaw fragments, and a mandible—belonged to a creature that was clearly heading toward man as long ago as 20 million years. This would mean that the separation of our direct ancestors from those of the apes goes back at least a million generations. Thus we can say that we and the great apes are cousins, but "cousins a million times removed."

Although we share many characteristics with the apes, they differ from us in many details. These great differences are what we might expect when our separation from a common stem goes back such a long time.

We do not yet know as much as we would wish about *Kenyapithecus africanus*—limb bones would be especially welcome—but we do know that he was contemporary in East Africa with other fascinating primates. One was a small animal generally considered a close ally of the living gibbons; these are the most arboreal of surviving apes and today are confined to the Far East. An especially important creature was *Proconsul africanus.* This, many authorities once concluded, gave us an indication of the common stock for apes and men. We have good forelimb bones for it, and in 1948 on Rusinga Island Mary discovered a skull, the first nearly complete specimen ever found. Its canine teeth suggest an ape's, while its forehead reminds us of our own. It seems to me, however, to be neither an ancestral ape, nor yet an ancestor of man, but a side branch with characteristics of both stocks.

INEVITABLY OUR INTEREST QUICKENS when we think of finding clues to man himself, and of course we never know when that will be. One day in 1957, when Mary and I were hard at work excavating our best specimen of *Pelorovis*, our eldest son Jonathan left us and went off exploring on his own. Presently he came running back excitedly to us, urging us to go and see what he had found. When we asked him what it was, he said: "I don't know. It looks like a huge primate jaw. Perhaps it's the man we have all been looking for at Olduvai!"

You can imagine how thrilled Mary and I were. All of us had dreamed for years of the day when we might find a human fossil. We went quickly with Jonathan across the gorge. There, halfway up the other side, and partially uncovered, a specimen lay in the rocks. It certainly had all the appearance of a primate, but I did not think that it looked quite manlike—though, nevertheless, very exciting. We showed Jonathan how to set to work to excavate it, after photographing it in position. Slowly, and with great care and patience, he proudly uncovered his specimen. It proved to be the gigantic jaw of an extinct baboon, the biggest of all known fossil primates except, possibly, for a creature called *Gigantopithecus*, found in China as well as in the Siwalik deposits.

Jonathan's baboon—which I later named after him: *Simopithecus jonathani*—had a jaw as big as that of the modern gorilla, and even larger teeth, but it is clearly a baboon, not an ape. Its face was evidently

Extinct baboon, gorilla size, roamed East Africa a million years ago; now it awaits scientific description and a name. To reconstruct it artist Jay H. Matternes studied fragments of skull, pelvis, and limb bones. He drew the skeleton, basing spine and ribs on living species. Finally he added probable musculature and coat. Paleontologists of the Smithsonian Institution in Washington, D. C., call Mr. Matternes today's foremost scientific muralist.

high and broad, its muzzle short. Since that day we have found other examples of this creature, and also other types of large extinct baboons. An immense skeleton was found in 1962 by a young student named Margaret Cropper, who is now the wife of my son Richard. Her find, as yet unnamed, has a fairly long muzzle and all its bones are strikingly robust for their length. It is most unusual in body structure. All living baboons have legs a little longer than the arms, but in this fossil the arms are noticeably longer than the legs. Certainly a creature of this bulk must have shown more of the gorilla's deliberate climbing than the agility of baboons today.

Giant baboon remains occur at the famous site Olorgesailie, in the Great Rift Valley some 40 miles southwest of Nairobi. Here an ancient lake left deposits of white clays and marl, and here in 1942 we discovered a fantastic trove of artifacts. I had three days' leave from war-time duty as an intelligence officer. We were exploring the area on Easter Saturday. I was shouting to Mary that I had found hundreds of hand axes while she called me to join her nearby, and it turned out that she had found thousands! The men who made hand axes there by the lake hunted these baboons in great numbers, splitting the skulls to extract the brains and smashing the long bones for marrow.

How did they make their kills? We have found sets of stone balls in groups of three, which suggests that they may have been part of a bolas. Patagonian Indians placed similar balls in hide bags and tied them together with twisted thongs; they hurled this contraption at the legs of running animals to entangle them and bring them down. Some Eski-mos have used a lighter form for hunting birds. I think that our early hunters used this device, for we have never found any other weapon suited to attacking from a distance. Certainly to try to attack one of these gigantic baboons, hand to hand, would have been terribly dangerous.

What were they like, the fellow-creatures who looked at the animals around them with a considering eye and devised ways of hunting them —who brought lumps of red ocher to Olduvai and made tools out of the white chert there? Our evidence is accumulating.

Back in 1959 Mary discovered the skull of the creature we named *Zinjanthropus boisei*, a being with a long wide face, a very small brain and

Giant baboons symbolically confront four smaller relatives, the present-day Papio anubis, *on a granite outcrop in East Africa. This ancient form differed from today's baboons in limb proportion as well as size. Arms longer than*

the legs raised the creature's foreparts. At left, a big male sits quietly for a grooming session by a female, her smaller size inferred from living types. Another male, cheek pouches bulging with food, nibbles at herbs.

a very large jaw. This fossil clearly resembled the "near-men" (as I call them) found previously in South Africa by colleagues of mine.

Professor Raymond Dart discovered the first specimen in 1924 and named it *Australopithecus africanus,* "southern ape of Africa." Dr. Robert Broom and Dr. J. T. Robinson found and described many more, and it became clear that these were not pongids, or members of the ape family, but hominids, members of the family of man.

O UR 1959 SPECIMEN was the only fossil skull from Olduvai that was even faintly like man, and consequently we were prepared to accept the possibility that "Zinj" might have made the stone tools we found near him. Then, within months, at even lower levels in Bed I, we gathered more material. Mary found foot bones, a collarbone, and portions from fingers, and Jonathan uncovered a large portion of mandible. From these and other specimens we can identify another kind of manlike creature, which we now call *Homo habilis,* "man with ability."

Fossils of such importance require the most painstaking examination and thorough discussion. Experts naturally disagree — widely and vigorously — over these and other hominid remains. I should like, however, to summarize the situation as I see it today.

Physical qualities alone do not clearly distinguish man from other primates. An important standard for the genus *Homo* is the making of tools to a regular pattern. After painstaking study of the stone industries of Olduvai, Mary announced her conviction that *Homo habilis* produced them. At Olduvai we have found two distinct types of hominids. One we consider a true man, *Homo habilis,* not yet exactly like you and me in limbs and skull, but certainly moving in that direction. The other we now place with *Australopithecus,* a "near-man" that had diverged from us, who ultimately disappeared from the face of the earth and left no descendants behind him.

These types co-existed for thousands of years, and it may seem that this raises problems. Yet one forest may have five different kinds of monkeys, each making use of a different part of the available food supply and therefore not competing with each other. Similarly, we can assume that these two hominids did not come into conflict over food. Probably "Zinj" was mainly a vegetarian; this is strongly suggested by the wear on his teeth — which is like that of tribes who are predominantly eaters of vegetable foods. Probably *Homo habilis* was mainly a meat-eater, using stone tools to cut flesh from animals that he caught and killed for himself. Perhaps he also relied on robbing the kills of the larger carnivores and obtaining meat by joining the scavengers.

Above all, we regard *Homo habilis* as a true, though primitive, man who gave thought to the future and made tools for his needs. I think it is reasonable to assume that as our probable ancestor he had begun to observe the wildlife around him, not only in terms of fear or as a source of food for himself and his family but also with growing wonder.

Best known of Africa's fossil apes, 20-million-year-old Proconsul africanus *intrigues scientists, who have studied it for clues to the probable common ancestry of apes and man. The author's wife found the first nearly complete skull in 1948.* Proconsul *mainly roamed the savannas, Dr. Leakey believes.*

Treasure in Trust

Since Kenya set up its first national parks shortly after World War II, immense strides have been taken in the protection of East Africa's wildlife. Tanzania and Uganda have also established a system of park areas affording game total protection—strict regulations prohibit hunting and keep out settlers and pastoralists. In all, the three countries have set aside some 70 parks, game reserves, and sanctuaries.

The reserves and sanctuaries differ from the national parks in that they are not wholly sacrosanct, and governments can and occasionally do yield to human demands for more farmland and alter the boundaries. Local tribesmen are sometimes allowed to remain within their borders.

Several protected areas preserve the habitats of extremely rare or localized animals. The Gombe Park, for instance, protects the chimpanzees studied by Baroness Jane van Lawick-Goodall; Lake Nakuru National Park in Kenya was created primarily to safeguard the wonderful flamingo population there. Most of the reserves and sanctuaries are potential national parks, areas set aside for possible future inclusion in the parks systems.

Boards of trustees, made up of prominent citizens responsible to government, administer the national parks in all three countries. The degree of financial and administrative independence from the respective governments varies, but on the whole the trustees are not under undue pressure or interference. Moreover, they have the overwhelming support of world opinion, a valuable asset in their struggle to save the wild creatures.

Within the last century, threats to East Africa's animals have come from several sources—notably changes in land use. The spread of settlers and their livestock and the rapid increase in the African population, along with developments in agricultural methods, have destroyed habitats and forced the wild animals into ever smaller areas. In the 1890's an epidemic of rinderpest, caused by a shipment of Indian cattle that carried the virus disease, wiped out vast numbers of hoofed animals, both wild and domestic.

The tsetse fly has been responsible for the destruction of still more wildlife. It subsists on the blood of animals and carries sleeping sickness, one of Africa's most dreaded human diseases, as well as the similar nagana, which strikes domestic cattle. With the tsetse fly infesting large areas of the continent, veterinary and agriculture departments of several countries decided that the best way to combat these pests was to kill off their supposed hosts—the large wild animals. The flies, however, found other sources of blood in smaller creatures, and enough of the larger animals escaped to ensure the flies' survival. In the main the great slaughter was for nothing.

Trophy hunters—who came from all over the world—further threatened the animals, and at the same time firearms became increasingly available to the Africans themselves. Elaborate safaris were conducted into the interior; their camps often spread over an acre or more. One man, after killing 15 elephants in a single day, complained that the hunting had not been particularly good.

An often quoted, if probably exaggerated, estimate asserts that the number of large mammals in East Africa has been reduced by 90 percent since the end of the 19th century. The national parks, sanctuaries,

Sleek leopard in Tanzania's Serengeti Park perches in an acacia tree to watch for prey, ignoring sightseers in a zebra-striped bus. A dedicated wildlife conservationist for three decades, Dr. Leakey played a leading role in establishing a system of national parks in Kenya shortly after World War II. In recognition of his work, he was made a founder-trustee of these protected lands.

Lioness chases a Thomson's gazelle through a grove of fever trees in the Serengeti Park. Her sprint ended futilely as the antelope sped away at some 45 miles an hour—the big cat's top speed: 35 mph. With luck, visitors to East Africa's parks, riding in Land-Rovers and buses, may witness such stark dramas of the wild. During the dry season, when most larger herbivores migrate to the west, lions as a rule remain in their territories, feeding almost exclusively on gazelles.

and reserves are now struggling to preserve the remaining wildlife, but its survival is by no means fully assured.

Men of vision long ago became deeply concerned about the disappearing animals and began pressing for conservation measures. Lack of adequate funds—and indifference—however, prevented the formation of any permanent parks until near the middle of the 20th century.

In 1948 Kenya established Tsavo National Park, which spreads over 8,024 square miles of arid country. The largest national park in East Africa, Tsavo holds more than 70 species of mammals, with elephants by far the most commonly seen. Their numbers have increased considerably despite incessant poaching. The main road between Nairobi and Mombasa splits the park into two parts: Tsavo East and Tsavo West. In the western section, visitors are rewarded by magnificent views of Kilimanjaro looming in the distance.

Serengeti National Park in Tanzania—perhaps East Africa's most famous park—sprawls over 5,000 square miles in a vaguely Texas-like shape. The nearly treeless Serengeti Plain forms the heart of the park, merging into stretches of savanna dotted with flat-topped acacia trees and granite kopjes.

The lions of the Serengeti are justifiably famous, but even more spectacular are the eddy and flow of enormous herds of migrating wildebeest, zebra, and gazelle in search of water and fresh grazing land. Along the small rivers near Seronera Lodge visitors often can see leopards sprawled on tree branches in the shade. The number of large mammals in the Serengeti Park has been put at more than a million, and although I think that may be too high, the congregation of wild animals there is without doubt the world's most remarkable.

Murchison Falls National Park in Uganda offers one of Africa's most stirring sights: the Nile River squeezing through a rock cleft some 20 feet wide and cascading wildly for 130 feet in the waterfall that gives the park its name. Visitors travel to the foot of the falls in a launch that makes a seven-mile trip from Paraa. Crocodiles, hippos, and rhinos abound along the river's banks, paying little attention to the boat.

Game watchers' inn, Treetops stands high on columns amid pink-flowering Cape chestnuts in the Aberdare Park. Guests here see a parade of wildlife coming to drink, bathe, or wallow in the mud. At night, when many animals arrive, flood lamps provide artificial moonlight.

Anglers sometimes pull Nile perch weighing more than a hundred pounds out of the pool at the foot of the falls. Away from the river, between 10,000 and 12,000 elephants wander the 1,500 square miles of undulating grassy plains.

In a way, Murchison Falls Park owes its existence to the tsetse fly. An invasion of the area by these deadly insects shortly after the turn of the century forced the people there to move elsewhere. In 1952 the government declared the region, still largely uninhabited, a national park.

The coastline of East Africa has not been neglected in the drive to open more parks. In 1968 Kenya established marine parks and reserves at Watamu and Malindi along the Indian Ocean coast. Goggled skin-divers explore magnificent coral formations and swim among brilliant parrotfish and angelfish. Starfish, crabs, spiny lobsters, sea urchins, and sea anemones live in the shallows. In the same year a survey was carried out leading toward the development of marine parks in Tanzania.

Kenya's Nairobi National Park—just outside the capital—is by all odds Africa's most accessible wildlife haven. Visitors in the heart of the city can still occasionally hear the lions in the park roaring at night, an attraction I doubt any other city can offer.

Covering 44 square miles and crisscrossed by well-marked drives, the park holds a range of habitats from open plains to riverine forests and bush-covered gorges, and harbors a high density and great diversity of wild animals—many of which move freely across the park boundaries. The lions of the park have become so accustomed to visitors and their clicking cameras that often a pride will lie lazily dozing within a circle of tourist-filled cars and buses, apparently oblivious to all the attention paid them.

O NCE THE PARKS WERE INSTITUTED, development of tourist facilities within them began. Lodges, hotels, roads, and special viewing points have been constructed, but the increase in the number of tourists has made it exceedingly difficult to keep abreast of the demand for accommodations.

Perhaps the most unusual lodge in Africa is Treetops, in the Aberdare National Park. Supported by stout pillars, the hotel overlooks a water hole and a salt lick visited by elephants, rhinos, antelopes, giant forest hogs, buffalo, and many other creatures. Balconies and a rooftop platform give visitors an unobstructed view. At night, floodlights simulate the light of the moon and bathe the ground in a soft glow, illuminating the nocturnal activities of the animals.

Famous people from all over the world have visited Treetops. Princess Elizabeth became Queen of England while sleeping there. During her visit in February 1952, her father, King George VI, died, and the young Princess awoke a Queen.

Eric Sherbrooke Walker and his wife, who built the original Treetops in 1932, tell many amusing stories of their observations and adventures

Standing on the rooftop viewing platform at Treetops, first hotel of its kind in East Africa, Mrs. Melville Bell Grosvenor watches elephants 40 feet below. To reach Treetops, visitors follow a path flanked by stockades where they can duck to safety if an elephant or a rhino comes too close.

Overleaf: Probing with their sensitive trunks, elephants at Treetops search in mud for salt and other minerals before ambling to the water hole for a late-afternoon spray bath. Another group saunters from the forest; it waited until the first moved to the pool before taking its turn at the salty area.

GERTRUDE G. GAYLEY

through the years. For instance, they once watched a baboon snatch a handbag from a lady on the balcony. Emptying the contents on the ground, he scampered off with a small bottle of perfume, after tasting and discarding a powder puff.

ALTHOUGH MUCH PROGRESS has been made in the protection of East African wildlife, the problems have been enormous. One, now almost overcome, is the attitude of the Africans themselves. For many years they felt, not without reason, that the animals were being protected so that visiting European and American hunters could undertake shooting safaris, and so that the governments could reap rich harvests of fees from licenses — all with no visible benefit to the people themselves. They saw these hunters spend $70 or more for a license to kill an elephant — an amount they could never afford — but if the Africans killed a crop-destroying elephant, the ivory was confiscated.

Now, however, more and more groups (including the East African Wild Life Society, government parks organizations, and a variety of others) are doing all they can to educate the population — especially the younger generation — to appreciate the reasons for conservation. Schoolchildren, many of whom live in well-settled areas and never see their country's animals in the wild, troop aboard buses for tours into the more accessible parks. The Frankfurt Zoological Society in West Germany has printed colored posters with Swahili text for display in Tanzania's villages. The text says that the whole world envies Tanzania its wild animals, and points out how much money tourists bring into the country. A mobile movie unit tours the villages with documentary films about the national parks, and competitions in the schools reward the best essays dealing with wildlife conservation.

As a result of these efforts, younger Africans have begun to accept the importance of preserving the continent's wild creatures.

When the countries of East Africa achieved independence, people in many parts of the world worried that the new governments would forget about the conservation programs, that park boundaries would crumble, and the remaining wild animals would be destroyed. Happily this was not the case. In many instances, the parks are better managed today than they were under the colonial administrations.

As one of the trustees of the board which set up Kenya's national parks, I feel most encouraged by the way things are developing today and by the very real interest which all three governments are taking in the expansion of the parks. Julius Nyerere, President of Tanzania, issued an inspiring statement at the Arusha Conference on the Conservation of Nature and Natural Resources in Modern African States in 1961, pledging continued support of conservation efforts.

"The survival of our wildlife," he said, "is a matter of grave concern to all of us in Africa. . . . In accepting the trusteeship of our wildlife we solemnly declare that we will do everything in our power to make sure that our children's grandchildren will be able to enjoy this rich and precious inheritance.

"The conservation of wildlife and wild places calls for specialist knowledge, trained manpower, and money and we look to other nations to co-operate in this important task the success or failure of which not only

Elephant poacher in a re-enactment of a capture splashes across the Galana River during

an ambush by Tsavo Park rangers. Poachers kill thousands of animals yearly, selling horns, skins, or ivory. Below left, a Waliangulu tribesman sights along the shaft of a poisoned arrow. A lesser kudu (below right), brought down by a poacher hidden in a tree, lies dead near a water hole.

ALAN ROOT

Poachers undergo questioning near the Tsavo River in a capture restaged for a documentary film. The rangers took the men prisoner and confiscated rhino horn and 60-pound elephant tusks (below). Poachers, most of whom kill for meat, usually receive sentences of a few months to several years in jail. Much illegal ivory, sold to smugglers, goes to the Orient for use in carving art objects.

affects the continent of Africa but the rest of the world as well." He has also remarked, "Americans and Europeans have the strange urge to see these animals, and we must ensure that they are able to do so."

A continuing problem facing park administrators involves the Masai, whose growing herds of scrub cattle constitute a real threat to the ecology of many areas in East Africa. Among the Masai, the size of a man's herd determines his status in the tribe. The more stock he owns, the greater his wealth. The Masai bleed their cattle frequently and subsist in part on a mixture of blood and milk, killing the animals for meat on ceremonial occasions such as feasts for the young warriors. With the benefit of modern medical care for the Masai and better veterinary service, both the cattle and their owners are on the increase. The large herds, constantly on the move between water holes, quickly destroy grazing land and deplete water supplies, and the Masai look with longing on the broad reaches of the parks and reserves.

The case of Ngorongoro represents a possible solution to the problem. Numbers of Masai families—with their cattle—lived within the caldera and on the Crater Highlands when they were part of the Serengeti Park. There seemed, at the time, to be no great disadvantage to this, though people ordinarily are forbidden to live within park boundaries. Ample grazing existed for both wild animals and domestic cattle, and the Masai only rarely killed any game. Tourists, too, seemed to enjoy seeing the colorful Masai living their traditional lives within the park.

G RADUALLY, however, the Masai came into increasing conflict with the park's administration. They set fire to the grass at the end of the dry season, in accordance with age-old custom, to stimulate the growth of tender young shoots for their cattle. Often these fires got out of hand and the park authorities, naturally, objected.

The Masai, for their part, complained that the herds of wildebeest carried diseases that spread to their stock. They also resented the very idea of the park as wholly a white man's concern, which, they felt, deprived them of their rights. And so the conflict between man and wild animals at Ngorongoro came to a head.

Some of us felt that the value of the Crater and the adjoining southeast Serengeti as a wildlife sanctuary was so great that the Masai families there should be given adequate compensation and provided with land elsewhere; but the Masai—understandably—did not wish to move. In the end a compromise was assured by the government. The caldera and a corner of the Serengeti (through which runs Olduvai Gorge) were excised from the park and designated the Ngorongoro Conservation Area. To oversee the region Henry Fosbrooke, a government officer with a very great knowledge of the Masai and their problems, was appointed the first conservator.

So far the results of this experiment have been moderately successful. While the needs of the Masai have had priority within the conservation area, the present trend is toward balanced land use, with the Masai, wildlife, tourism, forest protection, water conservation all playing a part in the total pattern. In my opinion, however, a very real danger exists which few people seem to have recognized.

Elsewhere in Masai country, tribesmen have been encouraged to fence large tracts of land as their exclusive grazing areas and to give up nomadism. The government—eager to get the people settled—helps by drilling wells and laying pipeline for additional water sources. Thus, the destructive large-scale movement of the cattle becomes unnecessary. Furthermore, the Masai are being taught to graze different areas within their ranches in rotation and to improve the grade of the stock for a higher milk potential.

I have no doubt that within the next few years this concept of fenced zones will spread to the Masai in the Ngorongoro Conservation Area. If they adopt it, the value of the area as a game paradise will disappear forever, since fencing is incompatible with the presence of herds of migratory zebra and wildebeest or troops of elephant and rhino.

POACHING represents a further problem besetting the parks. It exists to a greater degree than many people outside Africa realize. While few would condemn the tribesman who kills an occasional animal to feed his family, the large gangs that raid the parks in trucks and Land-Rovers, killing hundreds of animals, are another matter.

Poachers kill crocodiles for their skins, rhinos for their horns, elephants for ivory, and many other species of game for hides or meat. They capture most of their victims with wire snares, setting thousands of these cruel traps in gaps of fences and near water holes. In open country they place them among thornbush. Antelopes, stampeded toward the line, are caught and strangled in the snares as they attempt to dash through. One drive may kill 30 animals or more.

Some poachers use poison-tipped arrows, firing from ambush near a water hole. The lethal poison, prepared from the bark and leaves of *Acocanthera* trees, acts quickly and does not spoil the meat.

Several of the parks have acquired light airplanes and radios for their rangers, but the difficulties of patrolling the vast areas remain acute— the equipment is expensive to purchase and operate.

Aerial surveys have proved effective. In 1966 a flight revealed a hundred huts near a boundary of the Serengeti Park. Lack of cultivation in the area suggested that the people were living by poaching animals that strayed outside. President Nyerere directed that the villagers be resettled to remove the menace to the game.

In 1967, the heaviest year of poaching up to that time in the Serengeti, 225 men were convicted of the crime—which carries a penalty of from a few months to several years in jail—and 1,400 steel-wire snares were destroyed, but hundreds of other poachers escaped detection.

Even the animals themselves present problems for the people trying to protect them. Elephants in particular, because of their great size, can do much damage. In one park, officials built a windmill-fed watering tank for them, but when it became empty during a lull in the wind, the animals destroyed the rig, windmill and all.

Sometimes, because of interference with the natural order of things, a species may become too numerous for the limited space allotted to it. Two alternate solutions have been proposed for keeping animal populations in balance within the parks: translocation and cropping.

Translocation involves capturing animals and moving them to areas where they are scarce. Antelopes, rhinoceroses, and giraffes have been

Courageous naturalist Dian Fossey huddles only yards away from a mountain gorilla on a forested slope in Rwanda. She has studied the great apes for more than two years, with financial support from the National Geographic Society. To win the animals' acceptance she imitates their behavior, often sitting and chewing leaves as they do. One curious male has even ventured close enough to examine her shoelaces.

ALAN ROOT

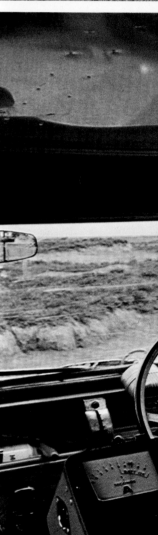

JOAN ROOT

Grasping the mane of a tranquilized lion, Dr. George B. Schaller of the New York Zoological Society helps an assistant affix a collar equipped with a radio transmitter; they must work quickly, for the animal will revive within minutes. The two will track the lion with a receiving set (top), recording his daily wanderings. Since June 1966 Dr. Schaller has observed the Serengeti's lion population. His study portrays a creature of massive grace, both savage and gentle, that reigns as a valuable member of the Serengeti community by helping to control the numbers of the hoofed animals.

Temperature-recording instruments inside Dr. Schaller's Land-Rover (below) pick up signals from a radio thermometer implanted in the neck of a lion. Howard Baldwin of Tucson, Arizona, monitors the panel. The thermometer revealed that a lion's skin temperature varies as much as 16° F. each day, depending on the cat's activities and the heat of the sun.

successfully translocated. Drug-filled darts, fired from crossbows or guns, immobilize even the largest animals and make them tractable. Moving the animals requires large numbers of men and trucks, and expense limits the effectiveness of the campaigns. I oppose the second method—cropping, or the killing of excess animals—except when it can be shown to be absolutely necessary, because in my opinion we still have too few facts about animal populations to justify such measures.

I N WHATEVER WAY the conflicting needs in East Africa are met, one thing is certain. The rapidly growing tourist industry, of great economic importance to the governments concerned, earns considerable revenue. In 1967 alone, more than 150,000 visitors, mostly armed with cameras, visited East Africa and left behind approximately $50,000,000. Thus developments in national parks or conservation areas that might hinder the growth of the industry will be strongly opposed.

Tanzania expects its number of tourists—now about 40,000 a year—to increase three to six times in the next decade. In February 1968 the Tanzanian Government signed a $900,000 loan agreement with the United States for importing equipment and developing all-weather gravel roads throughout its national parks.

Today the governments of East Africa have demonstrated that they consider their wildlife a treasure in trust, not only for their own future generations, but for all the peoples of the earth. The difficulties arise in implementing the measures they would like to undertake to make the national parks more accessible to the public and safer from the activities of poachers. These governments have, at present, somewhat limited financial resources and quite naturally must devote most of their revenues to such priority needs as education, health, agriculture, transport, and communications.

Various wildlife conservation programs are being financed increasingly by foundations, overseas governments, and by private individuals.

A good example of the kind of effective help individuals can provide is the gift of $30,000 from Mr. and Mrs. Nathaniel Owings of Big Sur, California. They gave the money in support of an African Wildlife Leadership Foundation project in 1968 to assist in developing the new Shimba Hills national reserve near Mombasa, Kenya. The reserve will assure protection for the sable antelope in the area.

Another significant contribution came from the World Wildlife Fund: $56,000 to help Uganda save the last of its white rhinos—fewer than 100 animals. With the money, a game warden, an investigations officer, and a team of rhino guards were employed to halt the depredations of poachers in the huge beasts' range northwest of Murchison Falls.

In a further effort to combat poaching the Frankfurt Zoological Society provided $5,000 to equip the rangers of Kidepo Valley National Park in Uganda with portable long-range radios.

I would like to stress that, encouraging and useful as these gifts are,

Cuddling a lion cub, Kay Schaller burps it after a bottle-feeding. Her husband found the weeks-old male emaciated and near death, abandoned by its elderly mother. As the cub slowly gained strength, he displayed behavior characteristic of young lions in the wild. He began to develop hunting skills by stalking and charging moving objects, clumsily swiping at them with his paws. After three months, the Schallers reluctantly gave the lion to a warden for eventual release in a park.

Overleaf: Blazing grass fire approaches a lion on the Serengeti. He lay without moving as the flames swept to within 10 feet. Herdsmen regularly burn off land to stimulate new growth, but this fire began accidentally, perhaps caused by a tossed cigarette. Animals often cross streams to escape the flames.

Helicopter-borne veterinarian, Dr. John M. King, head of the Capture Unit of Kenya's game department, fires an anesthetizing dart at a black rhinoceros on the Darajani Plains, where it risks death from poachers. When the drug takes effect—in 5 to 15 minutes—a ground team, called by radio, winches the animal onto a truck for transfer to a portable pen where it will receive an antidote. Below, captors weigh a 2,500-pound male on spring balances suspended from a baobab tree. Leather blinders protect the eyes from sun, dust, and chafing. This rhino remained in a holding pen for one month until its release in Nairobi National Park. In recent years Dr. King has captured more than 60 rhinos and moved them to protected areas.

VIC TOMASYAN

very much more help is nevertheless needed. The benefits of conservation will be reaped not only by the countries in which the wildlife survives, but also by the populations of contributing countries where adequate conservation came too late. This is particularly true of most of Europe, while the United States learned the lesson just in time and now protects much of its wildlife. Even so, Americans who visit the African parks should remember and report that the governments concerned need the greatest possible financial help at this stage.

Another encouraging note in the fight to save the animals is the increasing amount of research being done by various individuals and organizations on the habits, diseases, environments, and diets of the different animals. For with a better understanding of how the animals live, we will be better able to ensure that they *do* live.

Perhaps the Serengeti Research Institute at Seronera, Tanzania, does the greatest amount of significant work at present. Established in 1962 as the Serengeti Research Project, with financial support for buildings, equipment, and maintenance from the Fritz Thyssen Foundation and the Ford Foundation, the institute today serves as a permanent international center. Working facilities and family quarters are provided for scientists there, but they must obtain money for living expenses from outside sources.

The main theme of studies at the institute is ecology—the science of interrelations. Ecologists concentrate on the balance to be achieved between interacting factors in an environment. In Africa these factors are the human needs as opposed to the needs of the wildlife.

Specialists are examining the veterinary problems affecting the coexistence of man, wild animals, and domestic stock, and the productivity of soils and vegetation over long periods of time. Host-parasite relationships between certain animals and also the transmission of human and livestock diseases are undergoing further study.

As a start the Serengeti has been carefully mapped by aerial photography. Thirty rain gauges have been set up, meteorological data assembled, and geological and botanical surveys undertaken.

Scientists from all over the world have come to the institute to study many of the animals, including hyenas, lions, gazelles, antelopes, and buffalo. Such research projects are yielding extremely valuable information on methods of preserving the wildlife of Africa.

African game wardens, desperately needed to patrol the large parks, are being trained at the College of African Wildlife Management at Mweka on the southern slope of Kilimanjaro in Tanzania. A $25,000 grant from the African Wildlife Leadership Foundation in 1962 permitted the founding of the college; the Tanzanian Government provided buildings. The first year, 24 students, called cadet wardens, began studying such things as the feeding and migratory habits of birds and mammals; measures to combat fire and soil erosion; the use of firearms; operation and maintenance of motor vehicles; map reading; first aid, both for men and animals; conservation laws and ways of dealing with poachers; how to build huts, roads, small bridges, and dig wells; and finally how to keep records and administer a staff.

After the initial grant got the college started, more aid came from the U. S. Agency for International Development and from the British and

West German governments. Private donations came in from all over the world. In 1965 the United Nations made the college a special project of the Food and Agriculture Organization and assured it of support for at least five years. So far, more than 100 cadets have finished the two-year course and begun serving as members of their nations' conservation teams. Several graduates have been awarded scholarships for continued study in the United States.

All these efforts to save Africa's wildlife are very encouraging, and I hope they will prove successful. For it would indeed be a tragedy if one day—as H. R. H. Prince Bernhard of the Netherlands, President of the World Wildlife Fund, has said—our children's grandchildren should have to ask, "What was a giraffe?" or "What was a lion?"

One thing seems certain: In areas where animals are not protected in parks and reserves, there is little hope of preserving them in any numbers. A major conflict will always exist between them and the men who live by farming and herding, and eventually the animals must give way.

The interest which wildlife holds for the world can be assessed not only by taking into account the hundreds of thousands of tourists who have visited East Africa, but also by the popularity of films, books, and magazine articles dealing with animals in their natural habitats.

I most sincerely hope that as more and more people can travel to see wildlife in its natural setting, and more and more first-class films become available, the public will decide that penning up wild animals in zoos is out of keeping with the 20th-century attitude toward conservation. Once, perhaps, a case could be made for zoos on the grounds that otherwise the vast majority of people could never see such animals except in black-and-white photographs or as badly stuffed specimens in museums. Today those who cannot visit animals in the wild can see them in motion pictures, on television, and in excellent color photographs. Keeping wild animals in zoos seems to me to be no longer justifiable, whatever scientific benefits may come from it. On the other hand, it has to be admitted that such institutions as the Whipsnade Zoological Park in England and the San Diego Zoological Gardens in California are striving hard to give their animals better conditions.

Nevertheless, I cannot believe that anyone who has ever seen the superb creatures of the forest or the plains, free in their ancient home, can see them behind bars without a feeling of pity. The wildlife of Africa is indeed a treasure in trust, a treasure all of us must help safeguard for the generations to come.

As I complete this book, I feel sure that those of my readers who have previously visited East Africa will do so again if possible. Those who have not been able to come should do their best to make the trip. If a visit is out of the question, however, I am confident that they will still derive infinite pleasure from viewing the stately giraffe, the bounding impala, the lion, and the enormous elephant through films, on television, and in photographs in books such as this one.

Glow of sunrise silhouettes giraffes in the Serengeti Park. The future of such creatures rests in sanctuaries such as this and, even more, in the conscience of mankind. As man increasingly utilizes the animals' ancient domain, he must also work to conserve the heritage of a wild, free Africa.

GEORGE B. SCHALLER, NEW YORK ZOOLOGICAL SOCIETY

Index

Additional References

For additional reading, you may wish to refer to the following NATIONAL GEOGRAPHIC articles and to check the Cumulative Index for related material: T. Donald Carter, "Stalking Central Africa's Wildlife," Aug. 1956. Allan C. Fisher, Jr., "Kenya Says *Harambee!*" Feb. 1969. Alfred Friendly, "Africa's Bushman Art Treasures," June 1963. Thomas Garner James, "London's Zoo of Zoos," June 1953. Quentin Keynes, "Africa's Uncaged Elephants," Mar. 1951, and "A New Look at Kenya's 'Tree-tops'," Oct. 1956.

Bruce G. Kinloch, "Uganda's Orphans of the Wild," Nov. 1962. Hans Kruuk, "Hyenas, the Hunters Nobody Knows," July 1968. Louis S.B. Leakey, "Finding the World's Earliest Man," Sept. 1960, "Exploring 1,750,000 Years Into Man's Past," Oct. 1961, and "Adventures in the Search for Man," Jan. 1963. Baroness Jane van Lawick-Goodall, "My Life Among Wild Chimpanzees," Aug. 1963, and "New Discoveries Among Africa's Chimpanzees," Dec. 1965.

William M. Mann, "The Wild Animals in My Life," Apr. 1957. Melvin M. Payne, "The Leakeys of Africa, Family in Search of Prehistoric Man," Feb. 1965, and "Preserving the Treasures of Olduvai Gorge," Nov. 1966. H.R.H. The Prince Philip, Duke of Edinburgh, "Man's Wildlife Heritage Faces Extinction," Nov. 1962. Edgar Monsanto Queeny, "Spearing Lions with Africa's Masai," Oct. 1954. George and Jinx Rodger, "Where Elephants Have Right of Way," Sept. 1960. Edward S. Ross, "Hunting Africa's Smallest Game [Insects]," Mar. 1961. George B. Schaller, "Life With the King of Beasts," Apr. 1969.

Gertrude S. Weeks, "Into the Heart of Africa," Aug. 1956. Paul A. Zahl, "Face to Face With Gorillas in Central Africa," Jan. 1960, and "Mountains of the Moon," Mar. 1962. "The Last Great Animal Kingdom," Sept. 1960.

AVERAGE SIZES AND WEIGHTS OF LIVING ANIMALS OF THIS BOOK*

Last of the Giants

	Height (at shoulder)	Weight (in tons)
Buffalo, Cape	4½-5 ft.	¾-1
Elephant	9-11½ ft.	4-6
Giraffe	15-18 ft. tall	1-1½
Hippopotamus	4-4 ft. 10 in.	2-2½
Rhinoceros, black	4½-5½ ft.	1-2
white, or square-lipped	5-6 ft.	2-2½

Predators Great and Small

	Length (head and body)	Weight (in pounds)
Caracal	2-2½ ft.	15-30
Cheetah	4½-5 ft.	90-140
Civet	24-27 in.	35-40
Dog, Cape hunting	2½-3½ ft.	35-50
Fox, bat-eared	18-24 in.	7-10
Genet	16-22 in.	2-4
Hyena, spotted	3-4½ ft.	100-130
striped	3-3½ ft.	60-120
Jackal, black-backed	2-2½ ft.	15-25
Leopard	3½-4½ ft.	125-175
Lion	5½-6½ ft.	250-400
Palm Civet	17-22 in.	2-4
Serval	2½-3 ft.	30-35
Wildcat, African	21-25 in.	10-14

The Preyed Upon

	Height (at shoulder)	Weight (in pounds)
Antelope, Hunter's	3½-4 ft.	150-175
roan	4-4½ ft.	450-580
sable	4-4½ ft.	450-500
suni	12-14 in	18-20
Bongo	3½-4 ft.	350-450
Bushbuck	30-36 in.	90-150
Dik-dik	14-16 in.	7-10
Duiker, Abbot's	26-30 in.	25-30
gray	22-25 in.	30-35
red	17-19 in.	26-28
yellow-backed	36-42 in.	115-140
Eland	5½-6 ft.	1,500-2,000
Gazelle, Grant's	30-35 in.	130-158
Robert's	30-35 in.	130-158
Thomson's	24-29 in.	40-60
Gerenuk	36-41 in	60-75
Hartebeest, Coke's	3½-4 ft.	350-400
Jackson's	4-4 ft. 4 in.	300-375
Impala	34-38 in.	65-70
Klipspringer	20-22 in.	17-35
Kob, Uganda	3-3½ ft.	150-200
Kudu, greater	4-5 ft.	500-600
lesser	3-3½ ft.	175-230
Oribi	22-24 in.	30-40
Oryx, Beisa	3½-4 ft.	350-400
Reedbuck	30-35 in.	80-150
Sitatunga	3½-4 ft.	200-250
Steinbok	20-22 in.	20-30
Topi	4-4ft. 4 in.	275-325

(Continued next column)

	Height (at shoulder)	Weight (in pounds)
Waterbuck	4-4½ ft.	500-600
Wildebeest	4-4½ ft.	400-550
Zebra, Burchell's	4-4 ft. 3 in.	550-650
Grévy's	4½-5 ft.	750-900

Aardvarks to Zorillas

	Length (head and body)	Weight (in pounds)
Aardvark	3-3½ ft.	110-140
Aardwolf	26-30 in.	20-25
Bush pig	28-30 in.†	170-200
Elephant shrew, forest		
P. tetradactylus	6½-8½ in.	3-4 ounces
R. petersi	8-10 in.	6-8 ounces
Ground squirrel	8-10 in.	1-1½
Hare, Cape	14-16 in.	3½-4½
Hog, giant forest	30-35 in.†	300-400
Hyrax, *Dendrohyrax* (tree)	16-18 in.	5-7
Heterohyrax	15-18 in.	5-7
Procavia (rock)	15-17 in.	5-7
Mongoose, banded	12-16 in.	3-5
black-tipped	10-15 in.	1-1¼
pygmy	7-9 in.	6-8 ounces
white-tailed	22-27 in.	8-11
Pangolin, Temminck's	15-20 in.	14-18
tree	10-12 in.	3-4
Porcupine	20-30 in.	40-45
Ratel	24-30 in.	15-20
Spring hare	15-25 in.	5-7½
Warthog	25-30 in.†	150-200
Zorilla	10-15 in.	2-3

The Primates

	Length (head and body)	Weight (in pounds)
Apes		
Chimpanzee	M 31-37 in.‡	140-170
	F 28-34 in.‡	85-100
Gorilla	M 4½-6 ft. tall‡	300-400
	F 4-4½ ft. tall‡	165-240
Monkeys		
Baboon, olive	M 29-31 in.‡	48-66
	F 22-26 in.‡	24-33
Colobus, black-and-white	19-25 in.	10-15
Kirk's red	§	§
red	18-24 in.	§
Guenons		
blue monkey	21-24 in.	14-20
De Brazza's	12-14 in.	10-14
Schmidt's, white-nosed	12-21 in.	7-9
Sykes'	21-24 in.	14-20
vervet	24-28 in.	12-18
Mangabey, white-collared	17½-23 in.	7-12
Patas	M 23-30 in.‡	16½-27½
	F 12-15 in.‡	8½-15½
Prosimians		
Galago (bushbaby)	6-9 in.	6-10 ounces
Potto	12-16 in.	2-3¼

*Ranges include mature males and females.
†Height at shoulder.
‡For species with marked sexual dimorphism, M indicates males, F females.
§Size or weight not recorded.

Composition for *The Wild Realm: Animals of East Africa* by National Geographic's Phototypographic Division, Herman J.A.C. Arens, Director; John E. McConnell, Manager. Printed and bound by Fawcett-Haynes Printing Corp., Rockville, Md. Lithographic color separations by Beck Engraving Co., Philadelphia, Pa.; R.R. Donnelley & Sons, Inc., Chicago, Ill,; Graphic Color Plate, Inc., Stamford, Conn.; The Lanman Co., Alexandria, Va.; Lebanon Valley Offset Co., Inc., Cleona, Pa.; and Progressive Color Corp., Rockville, Md.